FROM RAINDROPS
TO VOLCANOES

DUNCAN BLANCHARD's life, like his book, has followed a trail with many crossing points—some quite unexpected. As a child he was determined to become an artist, but upon graduating from high school, in the midst of World War II, he enrolled in a course for apprentice toolmakers. After one rather unsuccessful year at toolmaking, he entered the Navy, was later commissioned an ensign and sent to Guam, where, he says, his interest in science began. One rainy night on his way to the Officers Club he found a soggy copy of a book called *Men of Science* in the jungle alongside the path. He dried it, read it, and for the first time began to understand what science was about. He decided to leave the Navy and pursue a scientific career.

Blanchard went back to school, received his B.S. degree from Tufts University, his M.S. in physics from Penn State University, and Ph.D. in meteorology from M.I.T. in 1961. He has been with the Woods Hole Oceanographic Institution since 1951, although field trips for his work in the atmospheric sciences have taken him far from Massachusetts—to Hawaii, the Caribbean, Costa Rica, and Iceland.

From Raindrops to Volcanoes is Dr. Blanchard's first book, although he is a frequent contributor to technical journals. About the writing of this book he says: "To put feelings into words is a skill that I highly respect, and one that I had little experience with prior to this book. It is a skill that we scientists have little of, but one we had better develop if we ever hope to breach that wall between science and the humanities."

From Raindrops to Volcanoes

ADVENTURES WITH
SEA SURFACE METEOROLOGY

BY DUNCAN C. BLANCHARD

ILLUSTRATIONS BY BERTON C. HEINRICH, JR.

DOUBLEDAY & COMPANY, INC.

GARDEN CITY, NEW YORK

1967

To
Duncan,
Becky,
and
Jonathan
who have just begun to explore
the wondrous world around them.

THE SCIENCE STUDY SERIES

This book is one of a number that will appear in the Series through the collaboration of Educational Services Incorporated and the American Meteorological Society.

The Science Study Series was begun, in 1959, as a part of the Physical Science Study Committee's program to create a new physics course for American high schools. The Committee started its work in 1956, at the Massachusetts Institute of Technology but subsequently became the nucleus of Educational Services Incorporated, of Watertown, Massachusetts, which has carried on the development of new curricula in several fields of education, both in the United States and abroad. The work in physics has had financial support from the National Science Foundation, the Ford Foundation, the Fund for the Advancement of Education, and the Alfred P. Sloan Foundation.

The purpose of the Series is to provide up-to-date, understandable, and authoritative reading in science for secondary school students and the lay public. The list of published and projected volumes covers many aspects of science and technology and also includes history and biography.

The Series is guided by a Board of Editors: Bruce F. Kingsbury, Managing Editor; John H. Durston, General Editor; and Paul F. Brandwein, the Conservation Foundation and Harcourt, Brace & World, Inc.; Samuel A. Goudsmit, Brookhaven National Laboratory; Philippe LeCorbeiller, Harvard University; and Gerard Piel, *Scientific American.*

Selected Topics in the Atmospheric Sciences

The American Meteorological Society, with the objectives of disseminating knowledge of meteorology and advancing professional ideals, has sponsored a number of educational programs designed to stimulate interest in the atmospheric sciences. One such program, supported by the National Science Foundation, involves the development of a series of monographs for secondary school students and laymen, and since the intended audiences and the standards of excellence were similar, arrangements were made to include their volumes on meteorology in the Science Study Series.

This series within a series is guided by a Board of Editors consisting of James M. Austin, Massachusetts Institute of Technology; Richard A. Craig, Florida State University; Richard J. Reed, The University of Washington; and Verne N. Rockcastle, Cornell University. The Society solicits manuscripts on various topics in the atmospheric sciences by distinguished scientists and educators.

PREFACE

On the frontiers of science, from biology and medicine to geology, oceanography, and atmospheric science, significant discoveries are being made both by research teams and by the individual scientist. In this book I will introduce you to a small section of the frontier of the science of the atmosphere. In particular, I want to tell you about some experiments that have been done in an effort to understand what goes on in our vast ocean of air, especially when it interacts with the surface of the sea. The majority of the experiments can be carried out with a minimum of equipment. Some of the original experiments were more involved than the versions given here, but the results were the same. Many have revealed new facts about the workings of nature.

I hope that you will become sufficiently interested to try some of these experiments for yourself. Do not mind if others have done them before you. You still can have the excitement of that special moment when you realize that an experiment is demonstrating something you may have heard about but have never seen before. You need only one qualification—curiosity.

If you scan the chapter headings, you will note that they begin with raindrops and end with volcanic eruptions in the sea. How, you may ask, did I ever decide to discuss two subjects that appear to have no connection with each other? Was it a random selection of a few topics from many? The answer is simply that I have chosen to write in a chronological way about the subjects that I know best, the ones with which I have been associated. My research work began, about seventeen years ago, on raindrops. That work led to something else, and before I knew it I was working on subjects that on the surface appeared to have no obvious connection with raindrops. Yet there was a discernible trail that led from one subject to the other.

In taking you along parts of this trail I hope to convince you that this is the way all science operates. Each scientist follows a trail of his own choosing. Some will be more daring than others and will leave the main trail to push deep into the unknown. Some will be content to follow the trails of others, hoping to find along the way interesting things that have been overlooked by those who came first. Some will travel together, helping each other when the trail is difficult. But all have one thing in common; they are curious creatures who wish to understand the workings of nature.

As we follow the trail in this book, I hope you will become interested enough to strike out on your own. You will be surprised to find that you can begin your exploration in almost any spot that you wish. It can begin in your home, your backyard, on any pond or lake, or at the edge of the sea. It can begin any place, and once begun, you can follow it with enjoyment for a lifetime.

CONTENTS

Chapter 1

THE FLIGHT OF THE RAINDROPS

"Attend now, and I will explain how rain collects in the clouds above, and how the showers are precipitated and descend upon the earth." These words were written two thousand years ago by the Roman poet Lucretius. In his great poem, *On the Nature of Things*, he ranged over a vast number of subjects that included clouds, rain, thunder, and lightning. But, typical of the thinkers of his day, he never put his ideas to the test of experiment. Some were subsequently shown to have much merit. Others, however, were either so vague and general that they said nothing at all, or else they were little more than interesting and sometimes amusing speculations. For example, he said that one of the causes of rain was the wind pressing against "swollen clouds." And the cause of lightning and thunder? Lucretius reasoned that when clouds collide they produce sparks and noise, as sometimes happens when two stones are struck together.

But it is not my intention to criticize the writings of Lucretius. It is all too easy to look backward down the long corridor of time and find error in anything. The ancients were struggling against a background of fear and superstition to find rational explanations for a multitude of natural phenomena. We should not criticize those who make an honest effort to understand the world around them. Rather, we should criticize those (they appear to be in the majority in every day and age) who unquestioningly will accept

speculation and hypothesis before they have been put
to the test of experiment.

The Beginning of Raindrop Studies

The ideas of Lucretius and his contemporaries on
the formation of rain were carried down through the
centuries and little attempt was made to improve upon
them. Well over a thousand years went by, and nothing
was added to our knowledge of how a raindrop is
formed. It has been only within the past two hundred
years that detailed daily or weekly measurements of
rainfall, temperature, and atmospheric pressure have
been made. By the end of the last century this collecting of data was being carried out with such zeal that
the meteorological magazines devoted page after page
to tables of this information. The rainfall was measured with great accuracy and reported to the nearest
one-hundredth part of an inch.

In spite of the tremendous labors that went into the
thousands of measurements of rainfall, no one seemed
to ask the next questions: What are raindrops like?
How big are they? Are they all the same size? Do they
vary in size from rain to rain? Could I perhaps learn
something of their origin if I determine their size and
how they are distributed in rainfall? No one, I say, so
far as we know, thought to ask these questions until,
in the 1890s, a few men, one in this country and several
abroad, began to wonder what raindrops were really
like. I want to tell you about one of these men, about
the ingenious and simple method he developed to
measure the size of a raindrop, and what he found out
about rain.

Wilson Bentley was a farmer who lived in the small
town of Jericho, Vermont. But no ordinary farmer was
he. Although he had no formal education beyond the

public schooling available in Jericho and had his farming to attend to, he was somehow able to carry out a program of research on the mysteries of rain and snow. He is best known today for the thousands of beautiful photographs he made of snow crystals. But that is another story; we must stay with the raindrops.

In the year 1898 Bentley began his studies on rain, for he had "the desire to add, if possible, a little to our knowledge regarding rainfall phenomena. . . ." And add he did. For seven years, from 1898 through 1904, he made 344 measurements of the sizes of raindrops from seventy different storms.

How did he measure the raindrop size? Very simple; he let the rain fall for a few seconds into pans of fine uncompacted flour. If the flour was at least one inch deep, the raindrops did not splash, and each drop produced a dough pellet. He let the pellets dry and then measured the diameters. But what relationship was there between the size of the dough pellet and the original raindrop? Again Bentley showed his ingenuity, but we'll let him speak for himself:

> Drops of water about $\frac{1}{12}$ of an inch and $\frac{1}{6}$ of an inch in diameter, suspended from the end of a broom splint and from a glass pipette, respectively, were carefully measured, and then allowed to drop into flour from heights of from 12 to 30 feet. The smaller pellets ($\frac{1}{12}$ of an inch) were of so nearly the same diameter that it was difficult to detect any difference, although in some cases the pellets were slightly flattened by impact, with a corresponding slight increase in the longer diameter. The larger artificial raindrops ($\frac{1}{6}$ of an inch) produced pellets that were considerably flattened and had a longer diameter, exceeding by about one-third the diameter of the drop.

In 1904, Bentley published his findings in a scientific paper that is, in my opinion, among the very best

ever written on the subject. He found that the largest
raindrops are about one-quarter of an inch in diameter
(about 6 mm). He suggested that in some cases the
size was determined by the size of snowflakes within
the cloud—the flakes had melted before they got to the
ground. Bentley went on to tell how he had found
different sizes of raindrops in different types of storms.
He believed that there was a connection between lightning and raindrop size. And from an examination of
his hundreds of raindrop samples he deduced that rain
could have its origin either from melting snow or from
a process that involved no ice or snow at all. But sometimes, he concluded, the sizes of the raindrops indicate
that both processes may have operated at the same
time.

Although Bentley's paper was clear and well written,
his strikingly original work and ideas went unnoticed.
No one went out to check his measurements. No one
gave much thought to the questions he had raised
about the nature of rain. Nearly forty years passed
before anyone in this country continued on with the
work he had started. Finally, in 1943, J. O. Laws and
D. A. Parsons, of the Soil Conservation Service, utilized Bentley's flour technique and obtained more
measurements of raindrop size. Since that time numerous scientists in many parts of the world have used
the flour and other methods to discover much more
about the sizes of raindrops.

Other Ways to Measure Raindrop Size

Before we turn to what has been revealed in raindrop studies, I want to tell you about two other
methods that have been used to measure raindrop size.
These methods, like Bentley's, are extremely simple

and can be mastered by anyone who has the curiosity and desire to learn something about rain.

In 1895, Professor J. Wiesner of Germany exposed sheets of absorbent paper to the rain. When the raindrops fell upon the paper they were absorbed, and the size of the spots could be related to the original size of the raindrops. This method is in common use today.

A popular paper is the ordinary filter paper that can be found in any chemistry laboratory; circular sheets of Whatman's #1 paper of at least 15 cm* diameter have been a favorite of many scientists. If these papers are dusted lightly with a water-soluble dye, such as Methylene Blue powder (also common in the laboratory or the corner drugstore), the spots from the raindrops will be recorded permanently on the paper. And, I must warn you, they will be recorded on you unless you are extremely careful with the dye. Put the dye on the paper only out-of-doors or under a ventilating hood. You can treat the papers by putting them one at a time into a large Mason jar in which one or two teaspoons of the dye have been placed. With the

* Cm is the abbreviation of centimeter, one of the units of length in the metric system. In much of this book we use this system. It's in common use in the world of science, and is really much simpler than the United States system. The other units we will encounter are the kilometer (km), the meter (m), the millimeter (mm), the micron (μ), and the gram (g). The length units are related to each other by multiples of ten. Thus one kilometer = 1000 meters; one meter = 100 centimeters; one centimeter = 10 millimeters; and one millimeter = 1000 microns. As a result of these simple relationships, one can, without the aid of pencil and paper, convert from kilometers to centimeters, or to any other length unit in the metric system. Unless you're a mental wizard, you won't convert from miles to inches as easily.

In conversion to United States units, one kilometer = 0.621 mile; one meter = 1.093 yards; and one centimeter = 0.3937 inch. Since one centimeter equals 10,000 microns it follows that one micron = 0.00003937 inch.

In the metric system the unit of mass, the gram, equals 0.002205 pound.

cover on the jar rotate it to tumble the dye completely over one side of the paper. Remove the paper and eliminate any excess dye by snapping the back of the paper with the fingers. Afterward the treated side of the filter paper may not appear to have any dye attached to it, but believe me, it does. You will find out when you expose it to the rain.

A third method of raindrop size measurement utilizes screens. Some years ago I was looking for a way to sample the large raindrops that often fall from thunderstorms. The flour method was just a bit too messy in heavy rain. The use of filter papers was out, as the large drops would splash. And so I tried exposing metal screens to the rain. The screens, similar to window screening but with a much finer mesh, were coated with soot from an acetylene torch. When the raindrops passed through a screen, they left an indication of their size, for they removed a circular spot of soot and carried it along with them. Although this method worked fairly well, it had its drawbacks. First, the use of acetylene was somewhat dangerous. Second, the long, stringy, soot particles that were produced ended up not only on the screens but on everything else in the laboratory. Needless to say, I was not too popular in the lab while doing this work.

Dr. Wallace Howell and his co-workers, then of the Mount Washington Observatory, came to the rescue just in time. They improved the screen method by substituting women's nylon stockings (60-gauge) for the wire screen, and confectioners' sugar (powdered sugar) for the black soot! Nylon stockings and confectioners' sugar hardly seem proper apparatus for measuring raindrop size, but they do the job extremely well. If you decide to try the nylon screen method, go to the dime store and get a set of embroidery hoops of about 15 cm diameter. Mount a piece of the nylon screening tightly on the hoops and coat it with con-

fectioners' sugar. That's all there is to it; you're now
ready to go out and measure raindrops. But one word
of warning. The sugar may not stick at all well to stockings that are new. It appears that new stockings do not
carry the natural body oils as do old, worn stockings.
Therefore, unless you or someone else can wear the
stockings in, I recommend you "wear them in" artifi-
cially by dipping them (after they're mounted on the
hoop) into a trace solution of vaseline in benzene
(not more than a quarter teaspoon of vaseline in one
pint of benzene. Caution: benzene is inflammable).
This method is guaranteed to leave the fibers coated
with a thin but sticky layer of vaseline. You will have
no trouble in making the sugar stick to it. But shake
off any excess sugar before exposure to the rain. You
can easily retreat a used screen. Dip it in a pan of water
to remove the old sugar; let it dry, then sugar it again.

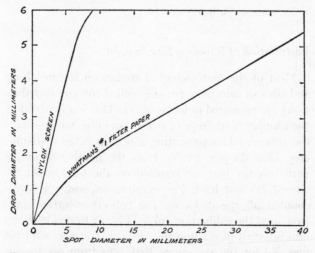

FIG. 1. The size of raindrops can be estimated closely from
the size of the spots they leave on nylon stockings or filter
paper. Graph shows the relations of diameters of spots and
diameters of drops.

The sugar-screen method will give you very nice rain-drop patterns. In Plate I you can see the clear, sugar-free spots that were produced when water drops of 2.65 mm and 5.4 mm diameter fell through the screen.

The relation between the diameter of the raindrop and the diameter of the spot that it makes on Whatman's #1 filter paper or on a sugared nylon screen (60-gauge) is shown in Fig. 1. You can see that the spots on the screens are not much larger than the drops that made them, but those on the filter papers are very much larger. This "magnification" of raindrop size makes the filter-paper method ideal for light rain where the drops are small. But in heavy rain, where the drops may be as large as 5 mm, it becomes intolerable. A 5 mm raindrop makes a spot 36 mm in diameter, more than seven times the size of the raindrop! A few such drops as these and the filter paper will look just as if it had been held under an open faucet. Better use the nylon screens for heavy rain.

Distribution of Raindrop Size in Rain

Most of the meteorological studies on the numbers and sizes of raindrops (usually called the size distribution) are presented in terms of N_D. This is a symbol for the number N of drops of size D per cubic meter of air, the subscript D representing a certain range of diameter. How do you get N_D from the number of drops (call this C) that are counted on the filter paper or screen? It's not hard. For example, suppose you have counted all the drops on the collecting surface and have used the calibration curve (Fig. 1) to divide them into intervals of 0.2 mm in true size. You may wish to find N_D for the size range that goes from 0.4 to 0.6 mm. If C is the number of drops in the size range, and T is the time in seconds in which the drops were collected, if A is the area (in square meters) of the collecting surface and S is the terminal velocity in meters per second (see Fig. 2) of these drops, then $N_D = \dfrac{C}{T \times A \times S}$. If you think about it for a while, you will see why it is so. You should make this calculation for each size range that you have collected. When you finish, you will have the size distribution of raindrops. Remember, this is the distribution of the drops in one cubic meter of space just above your sampling surface.

Now let's turn to what has been found out about the sizes and numbers of raindrops. In the past twenty years, measurements have been made in many parts of the world. It has been found, in general, that the more intense the rain the larger and more numerous are the raindrops. Now of course anyone who has walked in the rain (and who hasn't?) could make this statement. But without the benefit of measurement I doubt that one could guess that the number of raindrops per cubic meter of air varies from about 1000 in light rains (an intensity of less than 1 mm per hour) to 5000 or more in the heavier rains. The size of the raindrops has been found to range all the way from 0.2 mm diameter (by definition they have to be this large to be called a raindrop) to drops of about 6 mm diameter. These large drops usually are found only in downpours greater than 50 mm per hour.

It doesn't take very many of these giant 6 mm drops to bring a lot of water to the ground. Let's imagine two rainfalls where the number of drops per cubic meter of air are equal. In the first the drops are all 1 mm diameter, and in the second they are 6 mm diameter. There is much more water in the cubic meter of air containing the large drops. Just how much more is given by the cube of the ratio of the diameters,

$$\left(\frac{6}{1}\right)^3 = 6 \times 6 \times 6 = 216!$$

However, the 6 mm drops fall about 2.3 times faster than the 1 mm drops (Fig. 2). Consequently, the amount of water carried to the ground in a given time by the 6 mm drops will be 216 × 2.3 or about 500 times as much as that brought to the ground by the 1 mm drops. When we use the expression, "it's a downpour" or "raining cats and dogs," we are speaking of a rain which probably has a few of these giant drops.

It is the exception rather than the rule to find raindrops of all the same size in a rainstorm. Nor are they distributed in a random sort of way. One generally finds more small drops than large drops. If the rainfall is light, the largest drops may be only 1 mm in diameter, but as the intensity increases, larger drops begin to appear.

Shortly after World War II, a number of meteorologists attempted to express these facts in mathematical form. The equations they developed related the intensity of rainfall (which is easily measured by rain gauges) to the size distribution of the raindrops. For example, with a rain intensity of 25 mm per hour, the equations said that the largest drops would be between 5 and 6 mm but would be so rare that only one drop would be found in 10 cubic meters of air. On the other hand, drops less than 1 mm should exist in numbers of about 1000 per cubic meter of air.

For a few years all was well. But then, as more work was done on the measurement of raindrops, it became increasingly clear that for a given rate of rainfall the raindrop distribution could vary. In particular, it appeared that "cold" rain—that is, rain which originated from the melting of snowflakes—had an entirely different drop distribution from that found in "warm" rain, which evolved without the snowflakes. Cold rain contained relatively few but very large drops, while warm rain contained very many but small drops. The suggestion was made that the large drops in the cold rain resulted from the melting of large snowflakes. With this the study of raindrops came full circle, for Wilson Bentley had made this suggestion half a century before.

Evaporation, Wind, and Raindrops

But the picture is even more complicated. We recognize, as did Bentley, that many other factors affect the size of raindrops. The turbulence of the air, collision and breakup of the raindrops, wind, and evaporation all can influence the raindrop distribution. Take evaporation, for example. This will cause the drops to become smaller on their flight from cloud to ground. In humid air this effect may not be serious, but on occasions evaporation can drastically decrease the size of the raindrops. It can do even more; it can eliminate the raindrops completely. In the Hawaiian Islands, where the raindrops are relatively small, I have often seen rain falling in long dark streamers from the base of small clouds, but never reaching the ground. The phenomenon of complete evaporation is well known in meteorology. This rain is called virga.

Wind can influence the raindrop distribution. Even though it may not cause the drops to break up, it still can separate the drops according to size. You can demonstrate the basic idea to yourself. Take a handful of dirt or sand and throw it a few feet into the air when a light breeze is blowing. What happens? You will find that the larger particles will fall back very rapidly and strike the ground nearby while the smaller particles move along with the breeze to hit the ground much farther away. In an analogous manner, wind can winnow or sort out raindrops as they fall to the ground.

I well remember one occasion in Florida when I was using the nylon-screen method to measure raindrop size in a thunderstorm. My first sample was obtained

just as the first drops fell. There were not many of these
drops, but they were among the largest I have ever
sampled, 5 mm in diameter or larger. The sky was dark
overhead, and lightning and thunder were roundabout.
I quickly obtained another nylon screen to be ready to
sample in the downpour that seemed certain to arrive
within a minute. But it never came. After the first brief
flurry of giant raindrops the rain ceased. However,
rain began nearby and continued for some time. I have
often wondered whether this was a case where the wind
was sorting out the raindrops after they had fallen
out of the cloud.

The wind-sorting effect can be tremendous, as we
can illustrate by making some simple calculations. Let's
imagine we have a cloud 1500 meters (about 5000 feet)

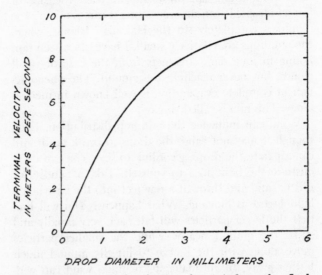

FIG. 2. The terminal velocity of a raindrop—the final,
steady speed it attains in its fall—varies with the diameter
of the drop up to a critical size. The change in the curve
to a straight line indicates this critical point to be at about
a diameter of 4.5 mm.

above the ground that is producing steady rain with drops up to 5 mm diameter. Imagine further that the wind is blowing at 4 meters per second and does not vary with height.

Although the larger drops fall faster than the small drops, they all are moved horizontally by the wind at a speed of 4 meters per second. Using the raindrop fall speeds given in Fig. 2, we can compute that the 5 mm drops are blown only about 660 meters to strike the ground at A (see Fig. 3) while the 1 mm drops are

FIG. 3. The wind can sort out raindrops according to size, much as it winnows grain. Small drop may hit ground at B hundreds of meters downwind from large drop at A although both drops left cloud together. This is a simplified version and it must be remembered that the usual changes of wind speed with height, both in the vertical and the horizontal, vastly complicate the situation.

blown 1500 meters to strike the ground at B. The drops of intermediate size will arrive, of course, at points between A and B. And so it is that raindrops of different sizes may be together as they fall out of a cloud and yet be spread out hundreds of meters over the countryside when they strike the ground.

But this is a simple case. If we were to be realistic about it, we would have to consider the variation of wind with altitude. Not only does the wind speed change as we proceed upward into the atmosphere but the direction (both in the horizontal and the vertical) changes as well. Sometimes updrafts or downdrafts cause the air to move vertically as fast or faster than it is moving horizontally. And, remember, the cloud also is moving. I have no intention of trying to solve one of these examples; my mental energy probably would be taxed beyond endurance. If we gave the problem to a computer, it would tell us that each raindrop in flight, according to its size, traces out a complex path that weaves back and forth through the air, sometimes in a spiral-like curve and sometimes in long graceful arcs.

If, in addition to the effects of wind, we were to introduce the other effects that have been mentioned, evaporation, turbulence, and raindrop interactions, the problem of what happens to raindrops as they fall is almost enough to tax even a computer! Yet these complexities must be overcome if we are to use the raindrop distribution on the ground to learn something about the initial formation of the raindrops.

Much work, both experimental and theoretical, has been carried out along these lines in the past fifteen years. Some scientists, in an effort to minimize these problems, have used airplanes or climbed mountains to enable them to take samples just as the raindrops leave the cloud.

In a sense, the raindrop size distributions are the fingerprints of a storm. Through them we may some day hope to type or classify the mechanisms by which rain evolves.

Chapter 2

WHO SAYS
A RAINDROP IS TEAR-SHAPED?

As a child in the Berkshire Hills of western Massachusetts I used to watch in awe the approach of one of nature's most spectacular performances—a summer thunderstorm. And what child, or adult, is not impressed with a performance, set upon the entire stage of nature, that opens with a darkening of the sky by boiling, rapidly rising clouds and is followed in quick succession by jagged flashes of lightning and the booming of thunder across the valley? All this was the prelude to the avalanche of rain sure to follow, and by then I was usually in the house peering out the window. The forerunners were large drops that splashed and left long tear-shaped patterns against the windowpane. As more and more drops arrived, the patterns began to merge together until the pane was covered with a continuous thin sheet of water.

That was many years ago, and it's doubtful that I gave any thought to how big the raindrops were, how fast they fell, or what shape they had. But years later, when studying raindrops in earnest, I began to wonder whether those tear-shaped patterns, which must have been observed by thousands before me, may have been at least partly responsible for the myth that raindrops are tear-shaped (see Fig. 4).

What? You don't believe it? You say you're quite sure that raindrops are tear-shaped? How sure? Have you ever really seen a falling raindrop—up close? Maybe

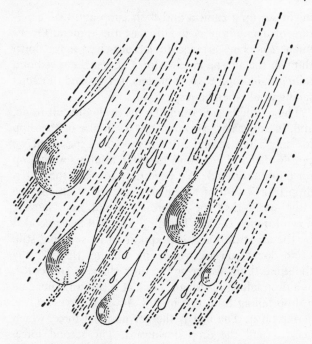

FIG. 4. The tear-shaped raindrop exists only on the artist's drawing board. Real raindrops, especially the large ones, tend to be flattened on the bottom, rounded on top, and wider than they are high.

you've seen many pictures of a tear-shaped drop. Or perhaps you once read that raindrops were tear-shaped and accepted it as fact. It is an unfortunate quirk that most of us will accept as absolute truth what appears on a printed page. But remember, the "truth" of a thousand printed pages, in gold letters if you wish, can fall as leaves before the wind in the face of contradictory results from a single experiment.

Let's do an experiment and see for ourselves what shape a drop of water takes as it falls through the air. I suppose there are a number of ways to do this. We might set up a camera and flash lamp and take a picture of a raindrop as it falls past the camera. Or we might somehow arrange to let ourselves move down through the air (on an elevator?) at just the speed of a falling raindrop, 2 to 9 meters per second. Picture-taking would then be easy.

These experiments would be relatively difficult to do, and, in any event, we would get a glimpse of the drop for only a few seconds. But there is an experiment we can do that will enable us to watch a falling waterdrop for minutes on end. We need only to place the waterdrop in a stream of air moving upward at exactly the same speed that the waterdrop would have moving down through the air. The drop will then be suspended by the air stream and will appear to be standing still.

No doubt you are wondering whether this is really the same thing, as far as the drop shape is concerned, as a drop falling in still air. Look at it this way: imagine a drop falling from rest in still air. Two forces will be acting on it. The first is the gravitational force, which acts to pull the drop downward. The second force, directed upward, is that exerted by the air against the drop. This is the same force that you experience when you put your arm out the window of a rapidly moving car. The faster the car is moving, the stronger will be the force of the air against your hand. And the same with the raindrop. As the drop accelerates from rest and falls faster, the resisting force of the air will become greater until, finally, this force is equal but opposite to that of gravity. The net force on the drop becomes zero, and that most famous of all laws of physics, Newton's second law, tells us that the drop ceases to accelerate. It is falling at a constant velocity. This is called the terminal velocity (see Fig. 2).

Well now, is there really any difference if we now imagine that the air is moving upward at this terminal velocity? The same force of gravity still acts on the drop, and the drop still moves downward at its terminal speed relative to the air. The answer is that from the point of view of the drop nothing has changed. But from our point of view the drop appears to be standing still.

A Raindrop Wind Tunnel

Enough of that. Let's build a vertical wind tunnel that will enable us to float or freely suspend large drops of water. The only materials we will need for this tunnel are a few pieces of wood, ordinary window screening, masking tape, and thread.

With the wood make a tunnel about 6 inches square in cross section, 4 feet long, and open at both ends. Unless the wood is fairly smooth it might be well if you use some sandpaper on the insides. About 18 inches from one end cut the tunnel into two parts; this will make it easier to work on the inside of the tunnel. The short section will be the upper part of your tunnel.

If you blow air into the bottom of the tunnel, it will come out at the top, of course, but it will be turbulent and bumpy. You must eliminate this turbulence. It can be done very nicely by making the air pass through common wire window screening (14×17 mesh). Take a pair of tin snips or scissors and cut out four or five square-shaped pieces of screening that are slightly larger than the cross section of your tunnel. Place them a few inches apart in the bottom part of your tunnel as shown in Fig. 5. You can put them into position faster than you can cut them out. Simply push them in from the top; since they are a bit larger than the tunnel, they will bow out a little, and the springiness of the screening will hold them tightly against the wall. When these screens are in position, the lower part of your tunnel is completed.

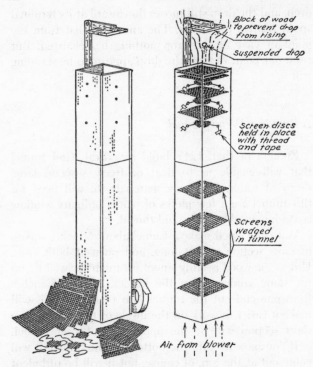

FIG. 5. Homemade wind tunnel can be put together with pieces of board, squares of window screen, masking tape, and thread, for experiments on waterdrops in air flow.

Now let's work on the upper part of the tunnel. For successful suspension of the waterdrops we must place the screening so that the air emerges from the top of the tunnel with its lowest speed at the center. We can accomplish this slowing down quite easily by adding some extra screens that cover only the center of the tunnel. Cut out some discs from the screening and tie four pieces of thread, equally spaced, around the edge of each piece. These discs can be held snugly in place by passing each thread through a tiny hole in the

center of each of the four sides of the tunnel and secur-
ing it with some masking tape. With this arrangement
you can make adjustments quickly and easily.

In my own tunnel I found that three discs seemed
to do the job reasonably well. I mounted them 3, 5, and
10 inches from the top of the tunnel. The top disc was
1.5 inches in diameter and the lower two discs 2 inches.
In addition to the discs you will want to place some
screens across the entire tunnel as you did in preparing
the bottom part. Place one between each of the discs
and finish up with two screens placed closely together
at the top of the tunnel. Your work is now finished.
Place the upper section on the lower section and you
will be ready to blow air in at the bottom.

A centrifugal-type blower driven by a half-horse-
power motor will give you more than enough power to
push air out the top of the tunnel at the required
speed of about 9 meters per second.* This speed can
be increased or decreased by taking screens away or
adding more screens at the bottom of the tunnel.

One last thing. A foot or more above the top of the
tunnel you should place some sort of an obstruction to
the air flow; a four-inch square block of wood will do
the job. Without the obstruction the drops will rise
slowly and be blown out of the air stream.

You are now ready to attempt to suspend a waterdrop in the air stream. Fill an ordinary medicine
dropper with water and hold it vertically over the top
of your tunnel. The open end should be down and
about 3 inches from the top of the tunnel. Slowly

* Perhaps a large vacuum cleaner could be used for the air
supply, but I have never tried one. If it does not provide enough
air you might experiment with a tunnel that is smaller in cross
section. I do know, however, that you can suspend a drop of
water for a second or two by using a vacuum cleaner to blow
air through a simple cylinder of about one inch diameter. You
don't need any screens in the cylinder; just place the drop in the
air stream at the exit of the tunnel.

squeeze out enough water to make a drop 5 to 10 millimeters across. This drop will cling to the end of the
dropper, prevented from falling by the upward-rushing
air stream. If at this point you suddenly lift the dropper
upward and out of the air stream, the drop should remain behind, freely suspended and floating in the
current of air (see Plate II).

The Real Shape of a Raindrop

Look closely at the drop. Is it tear-shaped? I think
you will have to agree that it is not. It tends to be
flattened on the bottom, rounded on the top, and is
wider than it is high. If you side-light the drop with a
strong light and use a good black background (a piece
of black velvet is excellent), the drop will be a thing of
beauty, shimmering and possibly vibrating as it falls
through the upward-moving stream of air. Plate III is a
photograph of one of these drops. The ten-pointed
star centered at the left-hand edge of the drop was
caused by a spot of light, reflected from the drop, that
struck the lens of the camera.

Why aren't these drops tear-shaped? Well, why
should they be tear-shaped any more than they should
be triangle-shaped, square-shaped, or rectangle-shaped?
Actually, scientists have known for at least sixty years
that large, freely-falling raindrops were shaped like
those shown in Plates II and III, but they weren't
completely certain why they were that way. It wasn't
until 1954 that Dr. James McDonald, of the University
of Arizona, solved the problem. He found that the
shape of a falling raindrop was controlled by delicate
interaction among the hydrostatic, aerodynamic, and
surface tension forces.

Let me explain these forces in relation to the falling
raindrop. The hydrostatic pressure at any point in a

liquid is simply that pressure which is caused by the weight of the liquid above it. When you dive deep into a lake, you can feel the effects, sometimes painful, of the hydrostatic pressure against your eardrums. The deeper you go, the greater the pressure becomes. This pressure exists in liquid objects both large and small and exerts itself in all directions. If you were small enough to dive into the top of a raindrop, you would experience an increase in hydrostatic pressure as you swam from top to bottom.

The aerodynamic pressures on the falling drop are more complicated. They depend on the exact shape of the drop, the speed at which it is falling, and the density of the air. But there is only one fact about the aerodynamic pressure on raindrops that I want to impress upon you. The pressure of the air against the drop is greatest on the bottom and least on the sides of the drop.

Manifestations of the force of surface tension are, I'm sure, familiar to you all. The old trick of floating a needle on a water surface, the "walking" of some insects on water, the rising of water against gravity in fine tubes, and the formation of soap bubbles all depend on what we call surface tension. It is not necessary to go into detail concerning the nature of this force. Suffice it to say that it is caused by attraction existing between the molecules of a liquid. The resulting force at the surface tends to hold the liquid together and resists any effort to make the surface larger. In the case of a falling raindrop the surface tension attempts to squeeze or form the drop into a spherical shape. The explanation is that of all geometrical shapes a sphere has the smallest surface for a given volume.

We are now in a position to explain why a raindrop is not tear-shaped. Let's begin by supposing that by some magic we could produce a drop that *was* tear-shaped. What do you think would happen to it? The answer is illustrated in Plate IV, a photograph of the breakup of a column of water falling from a glass tube (water from a faucet behaves the same way). The tube cannot be seen. For the photograph, I added a pinch of silver nitrate to the jar that supplied the water to the tube. The silver nitrate reacted with the small amount of sodium chloride that is always present in tap water to produce silver chloride. While this silver compound remained in suspension, the water appeared milky-white and was very easy to photograph. This is a good trick to remember if you try such photography. The remaining photographs in this chapter were obtained with this aid.

Note that the first drop of water in Plate IV (drop A) that breaks away from the water column is tear-shaped. Not a perfect tear-shape, but tear-shaped nevertheless. Now look at drops B and C. A fraction of a second before the photograph was taken they had been joined together and were in the same position as A is in now. In other words, the tear-shaped drop A breaks up as it falls and becomes drops B and C. For a fleeting moment B looks like a long, thin dumbbell while C, a larger drop, resembles a cylinder with rounded ends. But not for long. Under the force of surface tension drop B is pulled together and becomes the nearly spherical drop D. The same forces of surface tension help to transform drop C into the flattened drop E.

The shape of drop D, which is about 2 mm diameter, is determined largely by the surface tension forces. The smaller a drop is, the greater is the effect of surface tension with respect to the aerodynamic and hydrostatic forces. And so it is that raindrops of medium and small size, those less than about 2 mm diameter, are almost spherical in shape. The smaller the drop the more nearly a perfect sphere it becomes. If we were to look at the droplets of which a cloud is composed (they

are about 100 times smaller in diameter than a raindrop) we would not be able to tell by eye that they
were anything but perfect spheres. The all-powerful
surface tension force is in complete control here.

But how about the other end of the size scale, that
of the large and giant raindrops? These are the drops
greater than 5 mm diameter (see Plates II and III and
drop E in Plate IV). The situation is different here.
The large raindrop is in a rather difficult situation, and
is often on the ragged edge of disaster. The surface
tension forces are trying to hold the drop together and
keep it in a spherical shape, while the aerodynamic and
hydrostatic forces conspire to blow the drop apart.
The aerodynamic force establishes a low air pressure
region around the sides of the drop. The combination
of internal hydrostatic force and external low pressure
region causes the water to bulge out at the sides. This
tendency to flatten and bulge out is opposed by
surface tension. If the surface tension force is sufficient
to balance the forces of destruction, the drop remains
intact and falls with a shape resembling a hamburger
bun. But if the surface tension force cannot compete
successfully with the other forces, the drop widens and
breaks.

A vivid demonstration of the power of surface tension to hold drops together can be seen if you try to
inject a drop of soapy water into the wind tunnel. Soap
in water will reduce the surface tension to the point
where the giant drops simply cannot be held together.
You will find that in order to prevent the water from
being blown off the end of the dropper, you will have
to reduce the air speed in the tunnel. Then, if you're
lucky, you may succeed in suspending a relatively small
drop.

I hope you now appreciate the fact that the shape
of a raindrop is determined by a delicate balance
among these several forces. The larger a raindrop be-

comes, the more it departs from the spherical shape
and the flatter it becomes. It is never tear-shaped,
never was, and never will be. At least not when it is
in its equilibrium state and falling at terminal velocity.
About the only time a freely falling drop is tear-shaped
is at the moment it breaks away from a water column.
But then raindrops don't form that way! And even if
they did they wouldn't remain tear-shaped for more
than an instant. You saw in Plate IV how rapidly the
tear shape was destroyed by the surface tension.

Nevertheless, I'm afraid that the myth of the tear-
shaped drop is here to stay. We see it in cartoons,
posters, and advertisements. As I sit here writing, my
attention has been drawn for the first time to the raindrops in the poster that is on the wall before me. This
poster is entitled "Weather and Climate" and was pre-
pared as publicity for the scientific efforts of the
recent International Geophysical Year. But the raindrops—they are drawn with a tear shape! However, I
have no real objection. I must confess I am partial to
the tear shape. From an artistic point of view these
falling teardrops are more pleasing than a bunch of
hamburger buns. Besides, who would recognize the
hamburger buns?

Some Raindrops Break

The size at which raindrops in flight will break is
believed to be in the range of diameters between 5 and
10 mm. The conditions under which they break are not
very well known.

Plate V shows a giant waterdrop (with an equivalent
spherical diameter of 9.4 mm) in the process of breaking up in the wind tunnel. Pictures were taken on a
single film at the rate of 70 per second. The air flow
had been increased slightly to prevent the pictures

from overlapping and when the drop broke it was moving upward.

About eleven stages of the breakup process can be seen. Starting from the bottom, you can see that the drop is very much flattened. It is apparent that the forces of surface tension are losing the battle. Less than a tenth of a second later the drop has been blown into two parts that are connected together by a narrow neck of water. This neck divides into three smaller drops, and the breakup is complete. Thus, a single large drop has produced two relatively large drops and three small ones. This type of breakup is common, but there are others as well.

Another breakup, called the bag-type, is probably the most spectacular and dramatic one. For reasons not yet completely known, the drop will sometimes be blown literally inside out. This process begins when the bottom of the drop develops a slight concavity. This depression rapidly and cataclysmically develops to the point where the drop looks like an inverted bag or perhaps the canopy of a parachute. But this is just a transitory stage. The thin film of water comprising the "bag" or "canopy" is blown instantly into hundreds of tiny droplets.

The bag-type breakup can be seen in the wind tunnel. But I must point out that it occurs so rapidly that it cannot be seen with the naked eye. In one instant you will see a large drop and in the next you will see only a spray of mist being carried upward in the air stream.

In the wind tunnel, drop breakup can often be induced by introducing some turbulence into the air. This can be done by rapidly passing one's hand through the air stream under the drop. The drop will be blown apart under the wrench of impact of the turbulence.

Although scientists know that raindrops can break up, they are far from having a complete understanding of the details. These details can be important. Some years ago, the late Dr. Irving Langmuir, Nobel Laureate in chemistry, put forth the idea that rain could form in clouds by a chain-reaction process beginning with the breakup of a single raindrop. He argued that the drops produced by this breakup would grow as they fell and collided with the smaller cloud droplets. Finally, each of these drops in turn would be large enough to break. This chain reaction, if the conditions were right, could produce a prodigious number of rain-drops. Let's suppose that each raindrop on breakup produced ten drops. At the end of only ten stages of the chain reaction, the original raindrop would have multiplied into 10^{10} or 10,000,000,000 raindrops!* That's a fairly respectable start for a rain.

The chain reaction idea has never gained much favor among meteorologists. But then it has never been disproved completely. Dr. Langmuir assumed that the raindrops in a cloud would break when they attained a diameter of 5 mm. Was he correct? It all depends. If turbulence in the cloud is the same as turbulence in the wind tunnel when one passes one's hand through the tunnel air flow, then it may be that raindrops do break at that size. But is the air that turbulent? We don't know. Until we know a great deal more about the growth and breaking of raindrops, I'm afraid we'll

---

* 10^{10} is a mathematical shorthand that represents the product of ten tens all multiplied together. In a similar manner $10^2 = 10 \times 10$, $10^3 = 10 \times 10 \times 10$, etc. And $10^{-2} = \dfrac{1}{10 \times 10}$, $10^{-3} = \dfrac{1}{10 \times 10 \times 10}$, etc. With this system it follows (think about it for a while—see if you can prove it) that $10^2 \times 10^3 = 10^{2+3} = 10^5$, and $10^6 \times 10^{-4} = 10^{6-4} = 10^2$. It works the same way for other numbers. For example, $6^3 = 6 \times 6 \times 6$, $8^4 = 8 \times 8 \times 8 \times 8$, and $4^{-2} = \dfrac{1}{4 \times 4}$.

have to reserve final judgment on formation of rain by chain reaction.

There is much more to be said about raindrops. I hope, however, that enough has been said to encourage you to think about them and to try some of the experiments that we have discussed. I am sure that many curious and exciting facts about raindrops remain to be discovered. Don't worry about not having a well-equipped laboratory. You are much more important than the laboratory. Remember what Wilson Bentley on his farm in Vermont did with a pan of flour and a broom splint.

Chapter 3

THE ORIGIN OF RAINDROPS

In World War II, when meteorologists traveling with the armed forces were called upon to forecast the weather for battlefronts from the Arctic to the tropics, it was realized that rain could be produced in clouds whose temperatures were higher than 0°C (or 32°F). Prior to this time it was generally thought that most rain (if not all) originated from the melting of snowflakes. This theory, of course, would require that a cloud penetrate high enough into the atmosphere to bring the temperature of at least a part of the cloud to below 0°C. After the war two kinds of rain were recognized—"warm" rain and "cold" rain. The difference in distribution of the raindrop sizes in cold rain and warm rain was mentioned in Chapter 1.

Warm Rain and Cold Rain

The basic idea that is used to explain the formation of cold rain had been formulated before the war by Tor Bergeron in Sweden and W. Findeisen in Germany. Briefly, it goes like this: A cloud forms; as it rises up through the atmosphere the cloud drops attain temperatures of less than 0°C. They often supercool; that is, they do not freeze immediately, even though the air temperature may be as low as −20°C or −30°C. Still no rain. At this crucial point a few ice crystals appear among the supercooled cloud drops. The stage is now set for a rapid conversion of the liquid water in the drops into ice crystals.

How does this occur? It is a well-known fact that the vapor pressure of ice (a measure of the rate at which water molecules escape from the surface) is less than that of supercooled water at the same temperature. As a result, the waterdrops evaporate and the water molecules condense onto the ice. In other words, the ice crystals grow at the expense of the waterdrops. They begin to fall, to collide with and stick to other ice crystals. Snowflakes are formed. The snowflakes melt into raindrops when they fall into warmer air in the lower atmosphere.

Any explanation of the formation of warm rain could not rely upon the vapor pressure difference between ice and water because no ice was involved. Whatever the process, it involved only liquid water. Perhaps by introducing a few numbers we can see just what the basic problem regarding warm rain is.

Cloud drops are of a radius in the order of 10 microns, and raindrops are about 1 mm (1000 microns) in radius. Assuming that both cloud drops and raindrops are spheres (a good assumption, as we've seen in the last chapter) we can easily compute the volumes of the drops. We know that the volume V of a sphere of radius R is $V = \frac{4}{3}\pi R^3$. If we let the radius of the raindrop and the cloud drop be R_r and R_c, respectively, we can represent the volumes as $\frac{4}{3}\pi R_r^3$ and $\frac{4}{3}\pi R_c^3$. Dividing the volume of the raindrop by that of the cloud drop will give us

$$\frac{V_r}{V_c} = \frac{\frac{4}{3}\pi R_r^3}{\frac{4}{3}\pi R_c^3} = \frac{R_r^3}{R_c^3} = \left(\frac{R_r}{R_c}\right)^3$$

Our geometrical reasoning tells us that the raindrop volume exceeds that of the cloud drop by a factor represented by the cube of the ratio of the radii. Using the radii given we find that this factor is

$$\left(\frac{1000}{10}\right)^3 = 100^3 = 100 \times 100 \times 100 = 1,000,000$$

It takes about one million cloud drops to make a single raindrop. And there, quite simply, is the problem that faced the atmospheric scientist of twenty years ago. How is it possible for such a fantastically large number of cloud drops to get together to form each of the millions of raindrops falling from a cloud when it rains? And to make things more complicated, the explanation had to account for the fact that some clouds, especially those over the tropical oceans, can form and produce rain all within a period of 20 to 30 minutes.

You might wonder if it really is necessary to gather all those cloud drops together for each raindrop. Why isn't it possible for a single cloud drop to keep right on growing by the condensation of water vapor directly upon its surface? Won't our growing cloud drop become larger and larger until, finally, the updrafts within the cloud are no longer enough support and our swollen drop falls out of the cloud as a raindrop? Well, this idea has the classic beauty and simplicity that we associate with many of the great ideas of science, but, unfortunately, that's all it has. When put to the test of mathematics and of experiment, it simply does not work. A number of people who worked on this problem found that nature would be hard pressed to grow cloud drops by condensation to even as small a radius as 100 microns, and certainly could not be expected to produce a full-fledged raindrop of a radius of 1000 microns.

Little Snowballs and Big Snowballs

There was no way out but to accept the idea that numerous cloud drops somehow are brought together to coalesce into a single large drop of water. And so work began on the coalescence theory of rain formation. This theory can be made clear by comparing it to something I expect most of you have done at one time or another. (I know I have.) Have you ever stood at the top of a snow-covered hill, packed a ball of snow, and started it rolling down (Fig. 6)? What happened? Didn't the ball grow as it rolled over the thousands of flakes making up tne blanket of snow in its path? And didn't it move down the hill faster and faster, growing ever larger, to reach the bottom with a speed far in excess of its speed at the top, and with a volume many times greater? Perhaps your big snowball hit a bump* on the way down and broke into two or more pieces. Did each piece continue to roll onward, growing as it went? Interesting!

Do you see what I'm getting at? Imagine that the snow on the hill is a cloud and that each of the snowflakes is a cloud drop. The small snowball released at the top of the hill is an extra large cloud drop that begins to fall down through the cloud, and the large snowball arriving at the bottom of the hill is a raindrop. The growth of raindrops by coalescence requires the drops to fall through the cloud and to collide and coalesce with the cloud drops that are in the path of fall. In other words, each raindrop has its beginning in

* Can you guess what the bump is in our analogy? That is the turbulence that causes raindrops to break up. It illustrates Irving Langmuir's chain reaction idea. This, however, is not of direct concern to the coalescence theory. I mention it here only because we discussed it in the last chapter.

Fig. 6. The snowball rolling downhill grows by gathering up the snow in its path. Similarly, an extra large cloud drop coalesces with smaller cloud drops in its path and grows to raindrop size.

an *extra large cloud drop* that falls among the much more numerous, smaller cloud drops.

This theory was not new when attention was given to it in the late 1940s. But until extensive experimental evidence and theoretical argument for the existence of

warm rain were presented, the Bergeron-Findeisen ice
crystal theory held the stage. One of the difficulties in
the theoretical work was the problem of trying to compute just how fast a drop would grow by collision with
the smaller drops in its path. The computation would
have been a simple one were it not that some of the
smaller drops, even though they were directly in the
path of the approaching large drop, were swept completely around the large drop (Fig. 7) by the air stream.

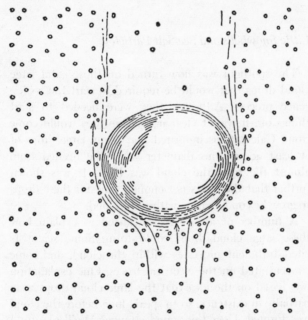

Fig. 7. Large drop falling through cloud strikes and cap-
tures some small drops in its path, but not all. Air stream
sweeps other small drops completely around large drop.

But no one knew just what percentage of the small
drops could escape capture, and thus no one could
make any significant calculations to support the theory

that coalescence could produce rain within a 20- or 30-minute period.

In 1946, Irving Langmuir and Katherine Blodgett, of the General Electric Company, opened the way for these calculations when they succeeded in deducing what these percentages (called *collision efficiencies*) should be. With their tables of collision efficiencies* the calculations of raindrop growth by coalescence were made, and it was found that the extra large cloud drops could indeed grow to raindrops in 30 minutes.

Little Snowballs and Sea-Salt Particles

The spotlight was now turned on those extra large cloud drops that would be required to start the coalescence process. Although they were needed to start things off, it wasn't clear just where they would come from. Calculations indicated that many large drops of at least 40 microns diameter would be needed from almost the time the cloud was born. It was shown further that there was not enough time for these drops to grow by condensation within the cloud.

A number of ideas were advanced to explain how these large cloud drops could form. Some scientists cited turbulent processes within the cloud, and some concentrated on the electrical forces. One explanation was based on the idea that the large cloud drops were partially in existence, so to speak, long before the cloud was formed. Does this sound strange? We'll see, for I intend to follow the trail of this last idea. We will start by going back to the year 1946 and to the Caribbean Sea.

Scientists of the Woods Hole Oceanographic Insti-

* Coalescence does not always follow collision. Some drops can bounce. The explanation of this behavior is still sought.

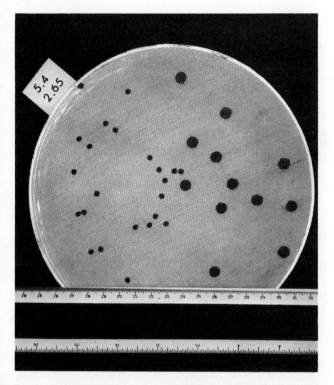

PLATE I. Sugar-coated nylon stocking on hoop shows spots left by waterdrops 2.65 and 5.4 mm in diameter. Scales are in centimeters (top) and inches.

PLATE II. Large waterdrop floats above homemade wind tunnel. Note that it is not tear-shaped.

PLATE III. Floating waterdrop photographed against black velvet background. Ten-pointed star is an optical effect produced by the camera lens.

PLATE IV *(at right)*. Tear-shape (A) appears, but only momentarily, when falling stream of water breaks into drops. Tear-drop breaks into B and C, which take final shapes D (the small raindrop shape) and E (the large raindrop shape).

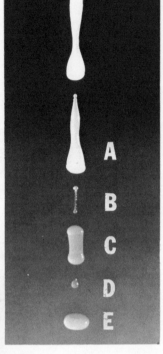

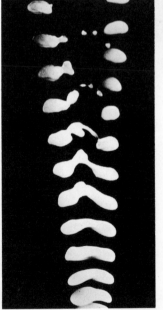

PLATE V *(at left)*. Breakup of giant waterdrop rising slowly in wind tunnel air stream is photographed at intervals of 1/70 of a second. At bottom, drop is intact. At top, less than 0.1 second later, it has broken into two large drops and three small ones.

tution, at Woods Hole, Massachusetts, had organized a Caribbean expedition to make temperature measurements in the sea and in the air. They hoped to use these measurements to prove some ideas about the exchange of heat and water vapor between the sea and the air. But after making the measurements, they found some extremely curious things in the way the temperature varied with height in the air. It looked as if there could be some source of heat in the air that had not been considered before. The co-leader of the expedition, Alfred Woodcock, began to wonder whether there perhaps were enough tiny drops of sea water or sea-salt particles drifting around in the air to provide the answer to their problem. Now I realize you are probably puzzled. How could those particles possibly have anything to do with the temperature of the air? Let me say only that when water vapor in the atmosphere condenses onto sea-salt particles, or, for that matter, onto anything, the so-called latent heat of condensation is released and the temperature of the air will rise. Does that give you a clue?

Woodcock began to search through the scientific literature to find out how much was known about the sizes and numbers of sea-salt particles in the atmosphere. He found that although it was known that they did indeed exist, surprisingly few measurements had been made, and absolutely nothing at all was known about their existence at heights where clouds form. And this in spite of the fact that, a few years before, a number of prominent scientists had engaged in some rather heated arguments about the connection between salt particles and weather! All of which proves, I suppose, that scientists are human, and sometimes will talk very knowingly on a subject about which they know little or nothing.

The Salty Air

When such a state of affairs is reached, the only sensible thing to do is to go out and make some measurements. That is exactly what Woodcock did. In the course of these measurements he discovered some interesting things about sea-salt particles. Some of the things he found, in fact, caused him to forget about the problem that had prompted him to study the salt particles in the first place! He began to wonder whether in some clouds the sea-salt particles might produce those extra large cloud drops that were needed to start the coalescence process of rain formation. The sea-salt particles should be found not only in air over the sea but perhaps in air that has passed over the sea and moved several hundred miles inland.

He made most of his measurements from a small, single-engine plane. His method of collecting the particles was straightforward, simple, and extremely effective. All he did was to open the window of the plane and push out into the air stream a small, thoroughly clean, rectangular glass plate. The plate was exposed for a number of seconds, during which time sea-salt particles would strike and stick to it. He took the plate back to the laboratory, where a microscope was used to count and measure the captured tiny particles. After many measurements he was able to compute the size distribution of sea-salt particles in the air over the sea. He found not only that there were large numbers of sea-salt particles immediately above the surface of the sea (which was hardly surprising) but that a great many of these particles were carried by the wind thousands of feet into the air, to heights where clouds formed. And this was unexpected.

The graph in Fig. 8 shows two distributions by size

of the sea-salt particles Woodcock found over the sea. One curve represents what was found at cloud base altitudes when the wind was blowing at 10 miles per hour (4.5 meters per second) over the sea; the other is for hurricane winds of at least 75 miles per hour (about 34 meters per second). Although the size distribution

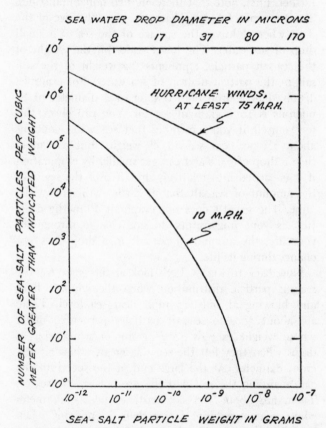

FIG. 8. The distribution of sea-salt particles in the air over the sea varies according to the speed of the wind. The curves show that the concentration of particles is greater for small particles.

for hurricane velocities was measured from a light-
house, the intense wind probably caused the particles
to mix upward and produced nearly the same distribution at cloud base level.

In case this is the first time you've seen a graph of
this type, let's learn how to read it before we go any
further. First, note that there are two horizontal scales.
The top scale, for drop diameter, gives the size of the
drop when it leaves the surface of the sea as a small
drop of sea water. The lower scale, for the weight of
the sea-salt particle, represents the weight of the sea-
salt in the particular drop of sea water. For example,
dissolved in a drop of sea water of a diameter of 80
microns is 10^{-8} gram of sea-salt. You can check this
for yourself if you remember that sea water contains
about 3.5 per cent sea-salt by weight. But remember
this: a drop of sea water can get smaller by evaporation
if it is carried into relatively dry air over the sea. But
the amount of sea-salt that it carries will remain the
same. The sea-salt does not evaporate from the drop.
Just as your fingerprints do not change throughout
your life, the amount of sea-salt in a drop does not
change during its life.

Now back to Fig. 8. Let's look at the curve for the
sea-salt particle distribution when the wind is light
and blowing at only 10 mph near sea level. There
are about 300,000 sea-salt particles per cubic meter
whose weight exceeds 10^{-12} gram, or whose size as
drops when they left the sea was greater than 3.7 microns diameter. At the large end of the spectrum the
giants among the salt particles are not exactly scarce.
There are about 100 salt particles per cubic meter
whose diameters were larger than 40 microns when
they left the sea! And look what happens when the
winds increase to hurricane strength. You'll find over
10,000 salt particles per cubic meter that were drops
with diameters of at least 100 microns! With such a

multitude of sea-salt particles in the air, no wonder we find the air very hazy over the sea.

And no wonder Woodcock became excited when he found so many large particles. He reasoned that these particles, being sea-salt, would absorb water vapor from the atmosphere as they rose through the humid air that is right beneath the clouds. Particles that absorb water in this way are called hygroscopic. Common table salt is hygroscopic; you must have noticed how wet and clogged a salt shaker becomes on a humid day (if you haven't, breathe several times on a few crystals of table salt and see what happens).

The atmosphere is like a giant salt shaker which the sea continually is filling with salt particles. Then, in turn, the atmosphere pours the sea-salt into the clouds. The largest of the salt particles provide the nuclei for the raindrops. They are the snowballs that you started rolling down the hill.

And the Salty Rain

Woodcock reasoned that if this idea was correct, then the rain that falls from a cloud should be slightly salty. Further, one should be able to predict just how salty it would be. You would go about it as follows. Fly in the clear air near the cloud and measure the size distribution of sea-salt particles; the air which goes into the cloud as it grows will contain these particles. Now go beneath the cloud and measure the raindrop-size distribution. Suppose you find the largest raindrop to be 2 mm diameter. And suppose that in the air outside the cloud you found the largest sea-salt particle to have, say, an amount of sea-salt equivalent to that in an 80 micron diameter drop of sea water. According to Woodcock, you could conclude that the large salt particle got carried into the cloud and grew to a 2 mm-

diameter raindrop by falling through and colliding with
the numerous non-salty drops.

We can compute what salinity the raindrop would
have. The volume of a 2 mm drop (2000 microns) is
greater than that of an 80 micron drop by $\left(\dfrac{2000}{80}\right)^3$
or about 15,600 times. But the amount of salt remains
the same. Thus the salinity of the raindrop would be
15,600 times less than that of the smaller sea water
drop (35,000 parts per million sea-salt) or $\dfrac{35,000}{15,600} = 2.2$
parts per million (ppm) sea-salt. Salinities of only a
few parts per million are low but they can be measured.

Woodcock and I went to Hawaii, in 1951, to test this
idea. Why Hawaii? Well, in the first place the warm
tradewind air that bathes Hawaii almost continuously
has previously passed over thousands of miles of ocean.
It is free of smog, smoke, and other contaminants that
air picks up when it passes over our towns and cities.
But because it has passed over so much ocean, the air
over Hawaii contains a plentiful supply of what we
wanted—sea-salt particles. Second, much of the rain is
warm rain, and it is produced from small clouds that
may be only 7000 or 8000 feet from top to bottom.
This rain is plentiful; in the rain forests of Hawaii it
rains between 300 and 400 inches a year (about ten
times the average rainfall in the continental United
States). With this much rain we didn't have to wait
around very long to get the conditions we wanted.

The most compelling lure was what we found on
the largest of the Hawaiian Islands. The island of
Hawaii has two magnificent volcanoes, Mauna Loa and
Mauna Kea, and both rise from sea level to nearly
14,000 feet. There are roads on the windward side of
the volcanoes, starting at sea level and running almost
parallel to the direction of the tradewinds to heights
of about 8000 feet. When clouds which looked as if

they might produce rain drifted up against the volcanoes, we could drive up these roads until we were very near the base of the clouds (Fig. 9). There we could

FIG. 9. Cloud base on slopes of Hawaii's 14,000-foot volcanoes can be reached by car for rain sampling.

sample the rain just as it emerged from the cloud. We didn't have to worry about all the problems one has when he samples rain on the ground far beneath the bottom of the clouds. (We discussed this back in Chapter 1.)

In this almost ideal situation Woodcock measured the salt particle distribution in the air outside the clouds, while I used the filter paper method to measure the raindrop-size distribution at the base of the clouds. In addition, we used large funnels to collect enough rainwater for a chemical analysis for salt. We found, in spite of the fact that the rainfall was often heavy, that the raindrops seldom were larger than 2 mm diameter. When we examined the rainwater for salt content, we found that it contained concentrations of a few parts per million. Many samples of rain-water were obtained, on days when there was much sea-salt in the air and on days when there was little, and on days of light rain and days of heavy rain. The day-by-day variations of raindrop size, sea-salt particle count, and rain salinity all were in the right direction to support the idea that the sea-salt particles had been the origin of the raindrops.

Does this give the seal of approval to Woodcock's idea? Well, yes and no. I have simplified the discussion and must now point out that there are complexities surrounding the whole problem. Nature is seldom as simple as we would like her to be. More work needs to be done before we can be certain that the salt particles behave the way we think they do. A very important experiment must be done; raindrops must be caught and examined, one by one, for their salt content. This is not an easy thing to do. Woodcock and Theodore Spencer, of the Woods Hole Oceanographic Institution, have tried; they succeeded partially, but their method will have to be improved upon. I'm sure that it will be, but until then we will have to withhold final judgment on the connection between sea-salt and rain. At the present time, however, the idea is the leading contender for the explanation of the production of warm rain in maritime regions.

I could not leave this subject without dispelling a notion I expect many of you may have after reading the last few pages. This is that there would be no rain at all from these clouds if the air contained no salt particles. If there were no giant salt particles in the air, the clouds might not produce rain as easily and quickly as they now do, but they would eventually. They'd just have to work harder. Some scientists think the clouds would grow larger and penetrate very high into the atmosphere. The cloud drops would continue to grow by condensation of water vapor upon them, and the cloud tops would probably reach freezing temperatures. At this point some ice crystals might form, and the cold rain process would take over. Or maybe enough large cloud drops may have bumped together by this time to make the giant drops that had been provided by the salt particles.

But this chain of events probably doesn't happen often. We always find sea-salt particles in the air over the sea. We know, of course, that they come from the sea. But how does the sea produce them? What is the mechanism by which the sea can produce such fantastically large numbers of particles, nearly a million for every cubic meter of air in the lower atmosphere over the sea? And why does the amount of salt in the air vary? For an understanding of these questions, we will have to turn our backs on the raindrops and the clouds and descend the trail that leads to the sea, the greatest expanse on the face of the earth.

Chapter 4

THE SURFACE OF THE SEA

Many years ago a delightful little book, *Flatland*,* was published. This is an imaginative piece of science fiction that describes the doings of the strange inhabitants of an even stranger land of two dimensions. Within this land the people lived and died, and only a few of the more curious ones dreamed and wondered of the extraordinary things that might go on in the imagined lands of one and three dimensions. Similarly, we who live in a real land of three dimensions also find it a far stretch of the imagination to conjure up any other world than our own.

But there is, in a sense, a land of two dimensions right here within our own world, and it extends for thousands of miles in the horizontal plane to cover an area of about 70 per cent of the surface of the earth. Yet its thickness does not exceed a tenth of an inch. I am referring to the surface of the sea, that incredibly thin sheet of water that separates the atmosphere from the ocean depths. All interaction between the sea and the atmosphere must occur across this interface.

It is well to keep in mind that the surface of the sea is neither sea nor air, and thus its properties are not necessarily characteristic of either. For example, the temperature, chemical nature, and electrical properties of the sea surface can be quite different from those of the air above or the water beneath. It is in

* It has been reprinted as a paperback book, and for one dollar can be obtained from Dover Publications, Inc., New York, N. Y.

this in-between land of sea and air where we must look to find the origin of the sea-salt particles.

In this chapter and several that follow, I am going to explore with you some of the curious things that are going on in this fantastic land of two dimensions. You will find, as did Alice in Wonderland, that things will get "curiouser and curiouser." If the inhabitants of Flatland could spend some time living on the surface of the sea, they would be subjected to a turbulent and stormy life. Not the least of their problems would be the possibility of a sudden, catastrophic expulsion across the border and into our land of three dimensions.

The Quiet Sea

Have you ever stood at the edge of the sea on a clear, quiet day and watched the reflections of the clouds and the birds? If you have, you must have been impressed with the rapidity with which the surface can change when a gust of air sweeps by. One second the water surface is a giant mirror reflecting the world above with a clarity that causes the water to appear as an inverted sky. The next second a gust of air will be bouncing along over the surface, leaving ripples that distort the mirror and its reflections into the crazy images of the fun house. This mirror of the sea has not been broken. It has only been twisted and momentarily distorted.

If you could examine the surface closely, you would find that it's a mighty busy place. Temperature differences between sea and air will cause heat to flow. And even if there were no temperature differences, water molecules would always be bouncing back and forth. This exchange occurs even when the air above the water is completely saturated with water vapor (a relative humidity of 100 per cent). But in the saturated case you will find just as many molecules entering the water as are leaving it. In other words, a steady state has set in and the air remains saturated. It's like a full subway train that pulls into a crowded station at rush hour. Many people may get off, but just as many get on, and the train leaves the station as crowded or saturated with people as when it entered the station.

The exchange of water vapor is extremely important for weather processes. Water vapor is the fuel without which we can have no clouds and rain. But these water molecules are not the large drops of sea water that produce the salt particles important (Chapter 3) in the formation of warm rain. To make a single one of these drops we would need millions upon millions of water molecules, plus a certain amount of salt. A concoction like this simply does not evaporate ready-made from the surface of the sea. We'll have to look for another mechanism to get the drops into the air.

Enter the Bubbles

As the speed of the wind increases, the waves become larger. At a speed of about 6 knots (6 nautical miles per hour), a few of the waves may become unstable, or else their tops will curl over and be blown off by the wind (Fig. 10). Regardless of how the waves break, large quantities of sea water fall or splash back into the sea. The stronger the wind, the more often this occurs.

Air is carried or pushed into the sea by the falling water, and within seconds the water near the surface has been transformed into a whitish mass teeming with bubbles. Just how the myriads of tiny bubbles are produced by the large globs of air that enter the water is a mystery that I do not profess to understand. But

FIG. 10. Whitecaps, which appear when the wind speed exceeds about 6 knots (7 mph), are the main source of bubbles in the sea.

produced they are. On occasions I have seen the water so full of small bubbles that it remained a milky-white for several minutes after the first appearance of bubbles. During that time they slowly rose to the surface.

Whatever the mechanism used by nature to produce bubbles, it is very efficient in producing extremely small ones. We have made measurements, near the seashore, of the bubble-size distribution produced just after a wave had broken. The bubbles larger than 0.5 mm diameter were present in concentrations of far less than 10 per cubic centimeter, but those smaller than 0.5 mm existed in concentrations of about 100 per cubic centimeter. The smaller the bubbles, the more numerous they appeared to be.

Are you interested in hearing how we made these measurements? I'll tell you for there's a moral (of sorts) in the story. Someone got the notion that it would be a great idea if we used an underwater camera to photograph the bubbles. So we borrowed a camera designed to take pictures automatically at great depths in the sea. Of course, we intended to use it at depths of less than a meter. The camera, light, and power supply were held together in two long, cylindrical cases. The entire thing was a bit awkward for one person to handle, but relatively easy to maneuver with one of us at each end.

Thus it was we waded out into the surf on a beach near Woods Hole. Edward Florence, who was working with us at that time, was lugging one end of the camera, and I the other. We held it in the water where waves were breaking and started taking pictures. We had our problems. The water surging back and forth against the camera tugged it this way and that. (Have you ever tried to hold a large object steady in turbulent water?) But our main problem came when we looked at some of the pictures. The camera had done too good a job! Not only did we see some bubbles (or what looked like bubbles), but we saw one or more of about everything that is churned up by the action of the sea along the shore. This included sand grains, parts and pieces of critters who had come to grief in the sea, and bits of seaweed. In short, we saw too much and it was never clear just what was what. But it was clear that we needed another "great" idea.

Eventually we found it, and it was simplicity itself. We made a watertight box of clear plastic, small enough to be held in one hand. One of the large sides was removable. At about the same spot where we had tried to work with the camera, Ed Florence filled the box full of sea water, and held it, open side down, just beneath the surface. When a wave broke and bubbles were produced, many of them rose up and into the box (Fig. 11) where they became trapped on the underside of the top cover. When enough had been collected, the bottom was attached and the box of sea water plus bubbles was carried out of the sea and onto the beach. There, with the aid of a small jeweler's lens, Florence counted and sized the bubbles. As he knew the speed at which bubbles of various sizes moved through the water, he was able to compute (in the same way we computed the raindrop size distribution in Chapter 1) the bubble-size distribution per cubic

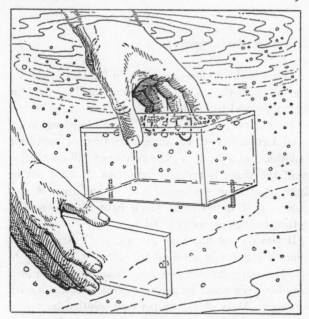

FIG. 11. Capturing air bubbles in the foaming surf for counting and measurement is easily done with a watertight clear plastic box.

centimeter of water. A simple plastic box had done what the camera could not.

The moral? Always tackle a problem in the simplest manner possible. If you don't, you may not be able to see the woods for the trees. In the case at hand, we saw all the trees except the ones we were looking for. I'm not saying that the camera should never be used for bubble studies. On the open sea, far from land, photography probably will prove superior to anything else. But for our work along the shore a simpler device was more effective. There's a time and place for everything. Half the problem is deciding just when is the time and where is the place.

Bubbles in the Laboratory

What is the connection between bubbles in the sea and drops in the air? Let's find out; we'll go into the laboratory and try to simulate conditions at the surface of the sea when bubbles are rising and breaking. We'll need a container of sea water, a method of producing bubbles, and a light. A glass container will do the job well; the shape is not too important. It need not be large; if it is 10 cm across and 10 cm deep, that is plenty. If it is too large, you'll have the problem of getting enough sea water to fill it.

If you do not live near the sea, you'll have to mix yourself a batch of artificial sea water. This is easy to do. For our purposes you can make what we call a poor-boy's sea water by mixing ordinary table salt with tap water. Make about a 3 per cent solution by weight (3 grams of salt per 97 grams of water).* You must use either this solution or real sea water in the experiment. Why? In salty water, bubbles that strike each other will bounce away; in tap water and distilled water they coalesce. This characteristic alone will make for profound differences in this experiment. So, if you use non-saline water, you will not see what I'm about to describe. Try it.

You'll need a good source of small bubbles. Many small bubbles can be produced by passing air through a fritted disc placed in the water. This disc is a porous, ceramic material at the end of a section of glass tubing; it can be obtained at chemical supply centers. If you

* You may find that the mixture is cloudy; this cloudiness appears to be caused by some additive that is mixed in with the sodium chloride. Boil it for several minutes and let it stand. The water will become clear as the additive coagulates into large particles which fall out to the bottom.

heat the tubing with a Bunsen burner, you can bend the softened glass into two right angles to form a U with the disc at the end of a short arm. Thus you can lower the disc into the water. An air supply giving several cubic centimeters of air per second will produce enough bubbles.

The final part of the apparatus is the lighting system. This is easy to set up, but it must be done in a particular way. I'm sure you've seen small dust particles flitting back and forth in a beam of sunlight like a swarm of fireflies. Although these particles are in the air most of the time, you see them only when the lighting is just right. You must be looking across or slightly toward a narrow beam of sunlight and into a black background.

You apply the same technique to illuminate the air in the first few centimeters above the water surface. For a light source you can use a strong flashlight, a microscope lamp, or a 35 mm slide projector. A piece of black paper or a box with the insides painted a flat black will make a good dark background. Black velvet is even better.

You're ready to begin the experiment. Make sure that the container is full of sea water and that the light is on. Turn off all unnecessary lights in the room and pull the shades. Look closely in the air just above the surface. What do you see? Nothing, I hope, except a void of darkness with perhaps a few stray dust particles drifting across the light beam.

Now turn on the air; here come bubbles from the disc.* Imagine that you're looking at a miniature sea, and that the bubbles rising to the surface have been produced by wave action. The bubbles have now

---

* In future experiments with the frit, I recommend that you keep the air on when the frit is in the water. Otherwise water will tend to back up into the numerous tiny pores, and it may be difficult to blow it out. After removing the frit from the water, leave the air on for a few minutes until all excess water is blown from the surface.

reached the surface and are breaking. Look again. Hundreds of drops, large and small, are rising from the surface to the air above (Fig. 12). The void of darkness

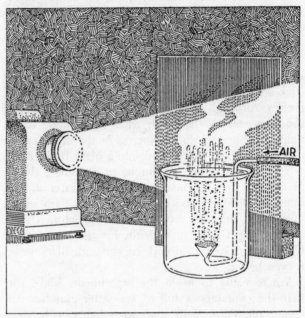

FIG. 12. The fog of drops ejected from bubbles breaking at the surface of the sea can be simulated in the laboratory (or at home) with this simple apparatus.

now resembles an animated Milky Way on a clear, dark night. The small drops are but pinpoints of light, and are in such profusion that they move through the air like smoke from a cigarette. The larger drops, which move much more rapidly, trace out an illuminated trajectory as they rise and then fall back to the water surface. Some get caught up by the breeze and are carried away with the small drops.

Are you quite convinced that bubbles are easily produced at the surface of the sea, and that they somehow can eject a multitude of drops into the air? Or are you skeptical of the demonstration? Especially of the fritted disc? You should be. Although the disc produces a great multitude of bubbles, which in turn break and eject drops into the air, this is not proof that bubbles produced by the sea will do the same thing. Maybe the bubbles in the sea are much larger. And if so, could it be that large bubbles do not eject drops into the air? We had better be concerned about this question, for we just might be led astray.

Fortunately, we can get an answer in less time than it takes to write these words. Do you remember what I said a few pages back about how bubbles are produced in the sea? They are produced by the splashing of water. Let's try it here. Dip up some water from the container, and then pour it back in with a great deal of splashing (Fig. 13). Hurry now; look in the water. Although the splashing may have produced some large bubbles, it produced many more small ones. Watch some of these bubbles as they rise to the surface. Can you see the tiny drops that are ejected into the air when each bubble bursts? The larger the bubble, the larger the drops and the higher they are ejected.

It seems clear that drops can be ejected into the air from bubbles that are produced when water splashes into water. You can let water fall into water from heights of one meter, 10 meters, or 100 meters. It makes small bubbles. Whenever waves break at sea and water splashes, small bubbles are produced. There's no getting around it; it seems to be a universal law. Even so, I, for one, do not know just what the mechanism is that produces the very small bubbles. Some day I'd like to find out.

Even single drops of water produce bubbles when they fall into the sea. Try the experiment for yourself. Take a medicine dropper, fill it with water, and let

Fɪɢ. 13. The easiest way to simulate the sea action that produces air bubbles is by pouring sea water into sea water.

single drops fall into your tank from heights of at least 30 cm. The standard medicine dropper that you'll find at the corner drug store will produce a drop about 4 mm in diameter. A drop this size should be large enough to produce some bubbles. Take a look. Do you see any? Move the dropper closer to the water to decrease the fall height. Do you still get bubbles? And how about drops smaller than 4 mm; do you think they'll produce bubbles, too?

While doing these experiments you must be sure that you have the optimum of lighting conditions. Then look carefully when the drop strikes the water;

you may want to use a magnifying glass. This effort will
be well repaid, for you will see some beautiful and
fascinating things. I will not tell you about them, except to say that sometimes you will see a vortex ring
of bubbles (analogous to a smoke ring in air) whirling
downward through the water. Why this forms in this
way I do not know.

Down the Stairs

This might be just the place to tell you about an
amusing experiment that we did nearly ten years ago.
We reasoned that if single drops of water could produce bubbles, then how about rain at sea? Rain is
nothing more than a collection of water drops of all
sizes. Perhaps the raindrops splashing into the sea
could produce many more bubbles than whitecaps do.
It seemed worthwhile to check.

A raindrop falling into water produces a lot of
splash. How about the production of bubbles when
these splashed drops fall back to the water? A good
question. Our problem was getting more complicated
by the minute. Not only might a raindrop produce
bubbles directly upon impact, but perhaps the splashed
drops could produce bubbles. Maybe more than the
initial drop. And how about the splashed drops from
the splashed drops? Does it ever end? Whoa! One problem at a time.

How does one start? One might begin by looking
closely for bubbles at the surface of the sea when it's
raining. But that's easier said than done. Have you
ever looked at a water surface when it's raining? It's a
pretty wild place. Your chances of spotting small bubbles with the naked eye are about the same as spotting
that proverbial needle in the haystack. At least he who
hunts for the needle needn't get wet while doing it.

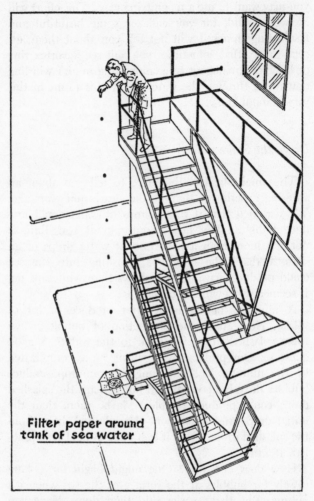

Filter paper around
tank of sea water

FIG. 14. The splash of a raindrop into the sea is simulated
by squeezing single drops from a medicine dropper into a
tank of sea water from a sufficient height (about 15 meters)
to let the drops attain terminal velocity.

We decided that this problem might be tackled by doing an experiment to simulate raindrops falling into the sea. We obtained a number of various-sized droppers that could produce drops of raindrop size, both large and small. A tank of sea water provided our "sea," and four flights of stairs provided a sufficient fall height for the drops to attain terminal velocity before they struck the water. Even the largest raindrops need only about 10 meters to attain terminal velocity.

We did our first experiment to find out how many splashed drops are produced when a raindrop falls into the sea. We let drops fall about 15 meters from the top of the stairs and into a small tank of sea water. The splashed drops were caught on large pieces of filter paper which we had placed around the edge of the tank. The experiment began with me or my co-worker, Ted Spencer, climbing the four flights of stairs with our assorted eye droppers. At the top of the stairs we'd take one of the droppers, fill it with water, look at that tiny target four floors below, check the flight path for wind drift, and then release some drops. Away they'd go! And then, if we were lucky, the flight would end with some resounding splashes (Fig. 14).

This type of experiment, and others in which we looked only for bubbles, told us a lot about bubbles and raindrops. We found, as you might expect, that the larger the raindrop the more bubbles were produced when it splashed into the sea. A 5 mm drop produced about 300 bubbles, most of which were less than 100 microns. Would you care to guess how many drops were produced by the splash of the 5 mm drop? There were nearly 1000, and they, in turn, produced about 2000 more bubbles. Adding it up, we get a total of about 2300 bubbles produced when a single large raindrop falls into the sea. We concluded that rain could indeed produce bubbles to compete with those produced by whitecaps.

Snow, also, was found to be a wonderful bubble producer. Alfred Woodcock let single snowflakes fall into a beaker full of sea water. Then, quickly, before any bubbles could rise, he placed a piece of glass on the surface of the water. The bubbles were trapped and he was able to count them. How many? He found up to several hundred per snowflake; as with the raindrops, the majority were smaller than 100 microns.

Although rain and snow are effective bubble producers, precipitation at any given time covers only a very small fraction of the total surface area of the sea. The area covered by whitecaps is appreciably larger. Thus we believe that on a world-wide scale whitecaps are the prime source of bubbles in the sea.

In the last chapter we found how sea-salt particles or tiny drops of sea water could act as nuclei for the formation of raindrops. In this chapter we have seen how bubbles are formed in the sea, and, if you did some of the experiments, you should be convinced that bubbles in the sea are able somehow to eject drops of sea water into the air. I say "somehow" because we have yet to take a close look at the amazing event that occurs when a bubble breaks. I was referring to this when I remarked, at the beginning of the chapter, about our inhabitant of Flatland and the dangers that he would continually face were he to live on the surface of the sea. If he should be caught on the surface of a bubble when it breaks, he'd be in for a ride the like of which he would not be likely to experience elsewhere—in his world or ours. Read on and see.

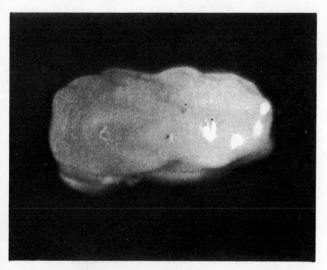

Plate VI. Collision of large waterdrop with smaller drops over wind tunnel produces waves on surface of large drop.

PLATE VII. Birth of bubble jet is shown in four stages (top to bottom). Bubble measured 1.7 mm in diameter. Total elapsed time was 0.0023 second.

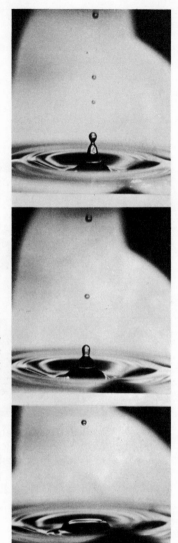

PLATE VIII. Life of bubble jet is shown in three stages (top to bottom). At top three jet drops are visible above fully formed jet. In center jet is collapsing. At bottom collapse is nearly complete, one drop still visible. Bubble producing jet was 1 mm in diameter. (Photos by Charles Kientzler)

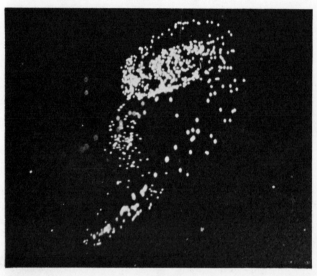

Plate IX. Condensation of water vapor in supersaturated atmosphere makes visible bubble film drops that ordinarily cannot be seen with microscope. Some 400 drops, produced by bubble 3.5 mm in diameter, are shown one centimeter above water surface. (Photo by John Day)

Chapter 5

EXPULSION FROM FLATLAND

Bubbles in the sea and bubbles in ginger ale (or any carbonated beverage) have one thing in common—when they break they both eject drops into the air. In the case of ginger ale you probably have been subjected to proof of this fact, although it's doubtful that you're aware of it. I well remember as a small boy how much fun it was to drink ginger ale, not so much because it tasted good but because, as we kids used to say, "it tickles our face." Little did we think that scientists, years later, would spend their days in a laboratory trying to understand the bubbles responsible for that curious tickling. Indeed, I don't think we ever gave any thought to the bubbles at all. If we did, we probably asked an adult and no doubt received the answer that is all too often given by adults to such "childish" questions—"It's caused by air currents," or "Ask your teacher. She's paid to know things like that." We settled for the simple fact that it tickled our faces.

If you haven't had this sensation when drinking a glass of ginger ale, I suggest you try the experiment. But before you drink, hold the glass up near a good light, and in front of a dark background. You'll see many bubbles breaking at the surface. Now look above the surface. Can you see the tiny drops that have been ejected from the bubbles? Some are thrown 10 cm or more into the air. These are the drops that you feel stinging your face when you drink the ginger ale.

That's all I wanted you to see; go ahead and drink up
the experiment.

Bubbles from Glass Capillaries

The time has come to zero in on these bubbles and
find out how drops mysteriously appear in the air when
a bubble breaks. There are things we can learn by
producing a series of bubbles all the same size, and
letting them break one after the other in exactly the
same spot. Primarily, we can find out whether all bubbles of the same size break the same way. The easiest
way to do this experiment is to produce bubbles by
forcing air through a fine glass tip.

I'll describe how these tips are made, as you may
want to try the experiment. You'll need some glass
capillary tubing, a Bunsen burner, and a pair of scissors.
Capillary tubing is simply thick-walled glass tubing.
Capillary tubing of 6 mm outer diameter and about
0.7 mm inner diameter is a convenient size. Take a
piece about 50 cm long, hold it at both ends, and heat
it at the center over the full flame of the Bunsen
burner. Rotate it slowly to heat it all around the middle.
In a short time the glass will begin to get soft and
will glow with a red color. At this point you should
remove it from the flame and quickly pull it apart, just
as if you were pulling apart a piece of hot taffy. If the
glass was hot enough, and if you pulled fast enough,
you'll end up with a long, thin, hair-like tube connecting the two ends. Break it at the center and you'll
have two capillary tips. Slide a piece of rubber tubing
over the large end of one of the tips, and make sure it
is attached securely. If it is not, you will have a dangerous situation. The pointed tip could be blown out at
very high speed when you try to force air through it.
Attach it with a hose clamp, or with a pair of pliers

tightly twist a few turns of fine wire around the rubber tubing.

Now, force air through the tubing (you'll need a pump or a compressed air bottle) and place it in water so that the tip is vertically upward and about a centimeter beneath the surface. Bubbles of all the same size will emerge, one after the other—maybe.

I say maybe, because one is seldom lucky enough to succeed on the first try. In the first place, the tapering tip that you made may be 20 or more centimeters in length and just too long to work with. No problem here; simply turn down the Bunsen burner to a low flame, heat the tip near the thick end, and draw it out again. You may have to repeat this several times, but you'll end up with a capillary tip only a few centimeters long which tapers to a fine hair-like point. And I do mean hair-like; this is no exaggeration. To produce the smallest bubbles, those less than 0.1 mm diameter, the tip will have to be about the size of a human hair. I remember that we once used some tips 4 to 5 cm long and so thin that they swayed with the breeze as I blew across them.

The scissors? Why do we need them? Well, sometimes the tip refuses to produce any bubbles at all, even when the air pressure is up to 30 pounds per square inch. When this happens, reach under the water with the scissors and snip off about a millimeter of the tip. Keep snipping until you cut back past whatever was obstructing the air flow, and bubbles once again will come from the tip. If the bubbles come one after the other, fine. You're all set. But if the air comes blasting out like a miniature jet exhaust, creating a hundred bubbles per second of a hundred different sizes . . . well . . . *c'est la vie!* Remove the tip from the water, turn off the air, and draw out a new one.

The bubbles produced by a particular tip will be larger than the tip, but, in general, the larger the tip diameter, the larger the bubble. The rate at which bubbles are produced depends on the air pressure and on the length of the narrow section of the tip. The longer this section, the slower will the bubbles emerge.

I remarked that the tip should be pointing upward when placed in the water. If you use a long, straight tip of the type we have been discussing you'll have to make a hole for it in the bottom of the tank. There's a far simpler solution. All you have to do is to heat the capillary tube a few centimeters back from the end of the tip and make a right-angle bend in the tube. Make another bend in the same direction a few more centimeters back. Your capillary tube is now J-shaped and you can position it in the water from above (Fig. 15).

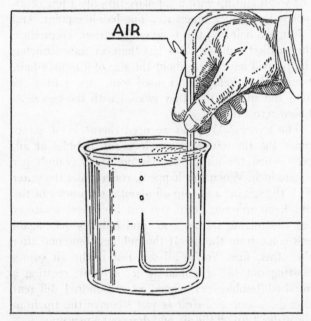

Fig. 15. A homemade, very fine capillary tip will blow underwater bubbles all of the same size. For the smallest bubbles tip must be size of human hair.

I have gone into detail describing the construction of these tips, because in the rest of this chapter (and in parts of later ones) we will discuss experiments that rely on them. If you want to try the experiments, you'll have to know how to make these capillary tips. But another reason for the detail is that I've wanted you to see how we tackle just one of the many little problems that have to be overcome in nearly every experiment. Perhaps I shouldn't use the word overcome, at least not in the making of these tips. We keep our fingers crossed every time we make one, and usually get what we want only after a long workout with the scissors.

I'll never forget a day when I was trying to make a tip that would produce bubbles of around 500 microns diameter. Do you think I could do it? I got everything else but 500 microns. I made one tip that produced bubbles of about 50 microns, and many tips that did quite nicely in the range of 100 to 300 microns. I had a few that performed very well in the 800 to 1200 micron category, and I even made some that treated me to some king-size bubbles of around 2 mm diameter. But not a single one obliged me with a bubble of about 500 microns. At the end of the day the lab bench and the floor were strewn with bits and pieces of glass. I left the lab that night muttering about "stupid capillary tips," wondering how I ever got into such a business, and thinking that maybe I should go back to that farm in the Berkshires.

But the next day, back at it again, I finally got a tip to produce 500 micron bubbles. Most things in life are not easy to come by. A capillary tip that produces bubbles of just the size you want is one of them. I wish you luck in your attempts. If you have problems, you have my full sympathy. If you don't, if you can make these tips with the greatest of ease, please let me in on your secret.

A *Flag in the Breeze*

Let's assume that you have a glass capillary tip that is producing a bubble of about 400 microns diameter, once every second. Shine your light over the surface of the water. You know where to look, for each bubble from the tip will rise and break at exactly the same spot. All right, ready now, here comes the next bubble. There—it broke—and instantly in the air above appear four or five tiny drops. These drops are exactly one above the other, and all directly over the spot where the bubble burst. The highest one is about 3 cm above the water, the next highest about 2 cm. They materialized so rapidly after the burst that we might almost call the two events simultaneous. But the most amazing thing of all was that they just appeared there in space, momentarily to hang motionless before they fell slowly back to the water. They certainly came from the bursting bubble, but why didn't we see them as they moved upward through the air? We can easily see them as they drift back to the surface.

We'll get to that question shortly, but now look again as other bubbles break. Exactly the same thing happens. The drops suddenly appear at the *same* height as the drops from the last bubble. Note the height attained by the highest drop, the top drop it's called. Every time each top drop from a succession of bubbles of the same size goes to the *same* height.

If you make another capillary tip, one that produces bubbles of about 200 microns diameter at a rate of 5 to 10 per second, you will be able to see a truly amazing sight. The top drop will appear at a height of about a centimeter, with the other drops at correspondingly lower heights. But, since many bubbles are breaking in the same spot every second, the drops from one bubble barely have time to get out of the way before the drops appear from the next bubble in line. If a slight breeze is blowing across the surface of the water (and one usually is), the top drops from successive bubbles will be carried through the air one after the other. So close and uniformly spaced are they that they look like beads in a necklace. As they are carried over the surface they fall at the same time; thus the "drop necklace" tilts downward. A small eddy or some turbulence in the air will cause a ripple in the line of drops, and the line will give the appearance of a flag waving in the breeze (Fig. 16). This flag effect is reinforced by the three or four other lines of drops lower down.

This is a remarkable thing. Such perfect lines of

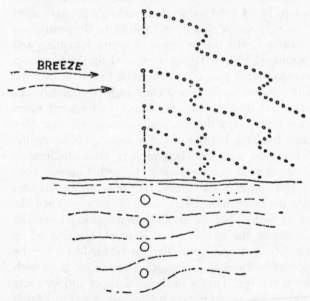

FIG. 16. The flag effect, produced when a horizontal breeze blows across a vertical line of water drops, is a vivid demonstration that bursting bubbles always eject drops to the same heights if the bubbles are all of the same size.

drops, and each drop in a given line appears to have originated at the same point in space. Here is a vivid demonstration of a property of bubbles of the same size: they eject drops in a manner that is reproducible from one bubble to the next. Would you care to guess how the bubbles do this?

The Bubble Jet

The drop necklace effect brings us to a curious phenomenon called the bubble jet. Let's briefly go back into the history of this jet, for it is a good example of how research trails cross, and how workers in one area of science often discover something which later turns out to be of great value in an entirely different area.

In 1927, C. W. Foulk, of Ohio State University, was concerned with the problems of steam formation and foaming in boilers. Trying to account for the tiny droplets that many people had observed in the air over the water in boilers, he took a close look at what happens when a bubble breaks. He found that several drops were tossed into the air, and he suggested that they came from the bottom of the collapsing bubble cavity. A few years went by. Then, in 1932, Otto Stuhlman, a biophysicist at the University of North Carolina, took up this suggestion and went one step further. He said that the drops most likely broke off from a pencil-like jet of water that he could imagine rising from the bottom of the bubble when it burst. He referred to the jets that rose from the cavity produced by the splash of a large drop of water. You can see these with the naked eye. Take a medicine dropper and let some drops fall a couple meters into a pail of water. Watch for the jet that forms. Better still, let nature do the experiment for you. The next time it rains, go out and take a close look at the splashes produced by large raindrops falling into a pond or a puddle. You will see what Stuhlman was referring to.

Neither Foulk nor Stuhlman concerned himself (in print) with the behavior of bubbles in the world outside boilers and laboratories. It remained for Woodrow Jacobs, who is now at the National Oceanographic Data Center, to realize the significance of bubbles in the sea. In 1937, Jacobs, who had been measuring salt in the air over the sea, was looking for the explanation of how the salt got there. He read about the work of Stuhlman, and it occurred to him that the bubble jet might provide the answer. After all, there was no doubt that whitecaps produced many bubbles of all sizes. If Stuhlman was right in saying that a jet was produced by a bursting bubble, and the larger the bubble the larger the jet, and the larger the drop it tossed into the air—then, thought Jacobs, here was a simple explanation why sea-salt particles should exist in a wide range of size over the sea.

A few years later the world was plunged into war, and it was not until around 1950 that research turned again to bubbles in the sea and bubble jets. About that time Alfred Woodcock (whom you met back in Chapter 3) was hot on the trail of the sea-salt particle. He, in turn, had read about Jacobs' hypothesis. The idea of a bubble jet appeared plausible, but was it really true?

At the laboratory in Woods Hole we spent many an hour peering through microscopes watching bubbles break. We came to one conclusion; if the drops were produced from a jet, then the jet was forming and collapsing far too rapidly to be seen by the naked eye. This was a job for the high-speed movie camera, with its reputation for seeing the unseen. In 1953, we obtained such a camera, and Charles Kientzler spent a fascinating summer taking movies of bursting bubbles. It was not easy. First of all, he had to learn how to

make the capillary tips to produce the bubbles. Then
he had to learn by trial and error how to illuminate
the bubbles as they broke; much light is required for
high-speed photography. And last, he had to develop a
technique to start the camera just before the bubble
broke. This was important, for this camera took about
three thousand pictures a second. It was nearly two
hundred times faster than an ordinary movie camera,
and, as a result, used up all its film in a second or two.
But Kientzler surmounted all these problems and
took many pictures of a bursting bubble. In addition to
the high-speed movie camera, he used a 35 mm still
camera with a high-speed electronic flash.

By summer's end Kientzler's pictures had removed
any doubt about the existence of a bubble jet. Foulk
and Stuhlman were right. When a bubble broke and
was in the process of collapsing, a vertical column of
water, wider at the bottom than at the top and looking for all the world like a miniature Eiffel Tower,
rose swiftly from the bottom of the collapsing bubble.

The birth of the jet can be seen in Plate VII. These
pictures were taken by the high-speed camera through
the side of a glass container. Starting at the top you
can see a 1.7 mm diameter bubble the instant before it
breaks. The horizontal dark line that runs across the
picture at the top of the bubble is the surface of the
water. In the second picture from the top, taken less
than a thousandth of a second later, the bubble is collapsing at the waist. The third picture shows it with
a peculiar conical shape, and the fourth picture, taken
only 2.3 milliseconds (0.0023 sec) after the bubble
started to break, clearly shows the jet which has suddenly appeared. Two drops are in the process of being
pinched off from the top of the jet.

The bottom picture was taken with the 35 mm still
camera. The camera was looking down on the surface
of the water at a glancing angle. The bubble, this

time only 1 mm diameter, has collapsed. You can see the jet with a drop just on the verge of being pinched off, and, in the air above, three other drops that earlier had come from the jet. They are one above the other, and moving upward at very high speeds. A bubble jet usually produces about five drops, one after the other, and all extremely rapidly. These drops are called jet drops; the first one to rise off the jet is referred to as the top jet drop, the second one the second jet drop, and so on.

In Plate VIII you can see, as viewed from above the water surface, additional pictures of the bubble jet. These three pictures show the jet fully formed, in the collapse process, and almost merged with the surface of the water.

Does the formation of the jet drops remind you of something else we discussed earlier? Look again at Plate IV, the photograph of drops forming from a downward-moving column of water. It's something like an upside-down bubble jet, isn't it?

The bubble jet is the beginning of many things. Here is the origin of the drops that "tickle your face" when you drink ginger ale. But more important, here is the mechanism that enables the bubble to eject drops upward at very high speeds. The reproducibility of this mechanism accounts for the flag effect (Fig. 16). And here is the origin of the haze of drops in the air above a bubbling surface, and, in particular, above the sea when whitecaps are producing bubbles. Here, many scientists think, is the origin of the drops that produce the sea-salt particles which eventually get carried into clouds where they help in the formation of rain.

Some Facts about Jet Drops

Stuhlman had noticed in 1932 that the height to which the jet drops were ejected varied with the size of the bubble. But he did his experiments in distilled water. Did the same thing apply when sea water was used? No one knew. At about the same time Kientzler was taking the first pictures of the bubble jet, Charles Keith, also of the Woods Hole Oceanographic Institution, used sea water and repeated the type of experiment that Stuhlman had done nearly twenty years before.

Keith found that the jet drops from bubbles of less than 1 mm diameter rose to exactly the same height found by Stuhlman; for larger bubbles the effect of the sea water was to make the jet drop go higher (Fig. 17). In sea water the height attained by the top jet drop increases with bubble size, reaching over 18 cm when the bubble is nearly 2 mm diameter. For larger bubbles the jet drop height decreases, and for bubbles in excess of 6 mm the jet drops are not even produced. Note that the maximum height attained by the second jet drop barely exceeds 5 cm.

Keith also measured the size of the jet drops. Unlike the ejection height, the size continually increased with the bubble size. A good rule-of-thumb is that the top two jet drops are of about the same size, and have a diameter about one-tenth the bubble diameter.

Let's consider one last fact about the jet drops, one which you may find hard to believe. It concerns the speed at which some of these drops leave the top of the jet to begin their upward journey against the force of gravity. It is exceedingly high, and if I mention it

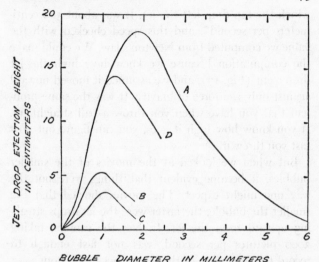

FIG. 17. Ejection heights of jet drops vary with bubble size as shown in these curves, where A, B, and C give heights, respectively, of top, second and third drops. The bubbles are breaking in sea water. Curve D gives height for the top jet drops from bubbles breaking in distilled water. Note that for diameters under 1 mm the type of water makes no difference in ejection height.

right now you may doubt my word or suspect a misprint. So we will work our way into it.

A bubble of 2 mm diameter ejects its top jet drop to a height of about 18 cm (Fig. 17); the same drop from a 0.2 mm bubble goes only a bit higher than 1 cm. Which drop do you think has the higher speed when it leaves the jet? The one that goes 18 cm up, or the one that can barely make it to 1 cm? It seems logical to choose the one that goes higher. Or does it?

Kientzler had taken high-speed movies of bursting bubbles of all sizes. The movies of the large bubbles (Plate VII) showed clearly the formation of the jet drops. From these pictures we obtained the speed at which the top drop left the jet. It was about 300 centimeters per second*, and this speed checked with the value we computed from Newton's law. We could make the computation because we knew how high the jet drop went (Fig. 17), and we assumed it moved upward against only the force of gravity. It was the same problem that you have when you throw a ball straight up. If you know how high it goes, you can figure out how fast you threw it.

But when we looked at the movies of the smaller bubbles, it became evident that things were not the way one might expect. The movies showed that the smaller the bubble, the faster were the jet drops streaking upward from the jet. In fact the camera, taking 3000 pictures per second, was not fast enough to record the formation of the jet and jet drops from a 0.2 mm diameter bubble. On one picture we could see the bubble at the surface, and, on the next, taken only $\frac{1}{3000}$ of a second later, all we could see were the jet drops in the air above the spot where the bubble had been. In less than $\frac{1}{3000}$ second the bubble had broken and collapsed, the jet had formed, and drops had been ejected into the air. But they went to a height of only about a centimeter.

Why this behavior? Why did these jet drops leave the jet so swiftly and yet not rise very far? Consider the first part of that question; I think the explanation of their high speed is to be found in the ratio of the surface tension forces (the energy source for the drop motion) to the inertia forces (which resist the drop acceleration). This ratio is high. That statement may be confusing but I'm not going into any more detail. In the first place, it would take a lot of space to expand

* Scientists often express centimeters (or meters, etc.) per second in mathematical notation cm $s^{-1} = \frac{cm}{s}$.

on it, and secondly, and more important, I'm not completely certain of the explanation.

But I am certain of the explanation of why these drops do not rise very high. They are small, and, as for any small object (for example, a dust particle or a fog drop), the terminal velocity is very low. If the drops are caused to move through the air at higher speeds, the frictional forces of the air become extremely great. Thus these small drops, which leave the jet with speeds far in excess of their terminal speed, undergo tremendous decelerations. These decelerations can be far worse than you would experience if you were in a car doing 100 miles per hour and crashed head-on into a very solid brick wall. But don't try this experiment. A jet drop can survive such decelerations. You won't.

Let me give you an example of extreme jet drop deceleration. We know from measurements that the top jet drop from a 70 micron diameter bubble breaking in cold water is ejected to a height of only 0.17 cm. Taking into account the frictional drag of the air, we have calculated that the drop moves upward from the jet with a speed of 8000 cm s^{-1} (about 180 miles per hour). But immediately the drag of the air causes it to decelerate at about 500,000 g's, and in only 0.00016 second it has risen to its maximum height, 0.17 cm. If it were not for the resistance of the air, and the drop had only gravity to contend with, it would coast on upward to a height of 335 meters, about 200,000 times higher than it actually does rise! Perhaps it is just as well that air resistance does slow down the jet drops. A trip at sea would be a harrowing experience with all those jet drops streaking up past you!

In this chapter and the one before, we have seen how bubbles are formed in the sea, how they break and form a jet, and how the jet produces drops that are suddenly ejected into the air above. The surviving jet drops ride the winds high into the air to be-

come the sea-salt particles that are always found above
the sea. In the next chapter we will see how a small
spider can help us catch small drops of sea water. We
will examine them closely and watch them change
into sea-salt particles.

Chapter 6

DROPS IN THE AIR

The technique that will enable you to capture the drops is simple and ingenious, and is one that the spider, for untold hundreds of thousands of years, has utilized for food-gathering. But the beginning of the story, as far as man is concerned, was only a little over one hundred years ago.

The Spider

In London, in the year 1847, there was a medical doctor named Augustus Waller. Dr. Waller was very much interested in raindrops, fog, snow, and hail, and the "vegetable and animal bodies" they might carry. Under the searching lens of his microscope, he found organic matter present in many forms of precipitation, but he was particularly eager to look at the minute drops of water that comprise fog.

How did he go about catching a fog drop? Dr. Waller tried one or two tricks that didn't work, and then the thought came to him that a ready-made fog drop catcher did in fact exist and was already in use. All he had to do to find it was to step outside his laboratory; the fog drop catcher he had in mind was a spider's web. As the fog drifts by, some of the drops should collide and stick to the fine threads or filaments that make up the web. He found this to be so; therefore, he removed the particular thread and drops and examined them under his microscope.

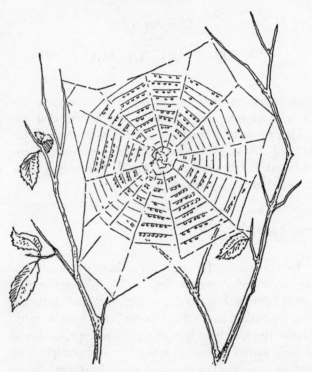

FIG. 18. The spider web gave Dr. Waller a ready-made fog drop catcher.

Perhaps you've looked at spiders' webs on a foggy day and have seen a necklace made of fog drops (Fig. 18). But be careful; many of these drops may not be fog at all, but drops of a sticky substance that the spider puts along the thread as he spins it. This adhesive helps in catching insects.

One hundred years went by. Dr. Waller's work seemed to be forgotten and became buried in the pages of a British scientific journal—the *Philosophical Magazine* for the year 1847. During all that time I don't think anyone ever used his idea.

But such an ingenious method was bound sometime to be discovered independently by other scientists. And it was. In 1946, Henri Déssens of France was searching for a way to catch small sea-salt particles in the air. He, too, thought of the spider's web. But instead of using a ready-made web, he caught a spider, brought it into his laboratory and induced it to wrap several turns of thread around a small frame. The spider obligingly went to work whenever Déssens wanted to capture some sea-salt particles. The frame and thread were taken out-of-doors and exposed to the air; any sea-salt particles that hit the thread stuck to it.

We have used the spider web method, à la Déssens, in a number of experiments at Woods Hole. I am going to tell you how to prepare the mounted spider threads, for I'm sure you'll have as much fun in working with the spiders as we do. Even if you don't catch drops, you'll learn a lot about the habits of a spider!

First of all, you'll need a spider. In the summertime, a spider hunt always will end in success if you look closely under the grass in lawns and fields. It may take several minutes, but have patience. In winter, you will find spiders in cellars, old deserted buildings, and barns. Select a small spider, one not larger than a millimeter, and put it in a box or glass jar. You'll see in a minute why we don't like to work with the large spiders.

The next thing you'll want is a frame around which the spider can wind its thread. A type of frame that I have used many times is illustrated in Fig. 19. It is made from a paper clip; if you use a pair of pliers you can very quickly rework a paper clip to make a frame just like it. There is no need to make anything more complicated. In science, as in every realm of human

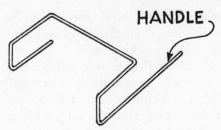

FIG. 19. Paper clip can be bent into simple frame around which spider can be persuaded to wind its thread.

experience, sophistication merely for the sake of sophistication is to be abhorred.

The winding of the thread on the frame is done as follows. Hold the frame by the handle between your thumb and forefinger, and about a meter above the floor. Put your spider any place on the frame. The problem now is to find a way to induce the spider to jump off. This can usually be done by tapping the frame lightly with your fingers. The spider, deciding that life might be easier elsewhere, will depart the frame in search for peace. But not wanting to burn its bridges behind it, it'll attach a fine thread to the frame. Down this thread to the floor it'll go, letting out more thread behind it. The next step is up to you. When the spider gets about halfway to the floor, start turning the frame and wind about ten turns of thread around it (see Fig. 20). If you're fast enough, you'll be able to wind the thread as rapidly as the spider produces it. If not, the spider will make it to the floor. And here is where it pays to have a small spider. A large one can move quickly and will easily leave you and the frame far behind.

One day I had such a large and nimble spider. As there were more experiments to do and it was the only spider we had in the lab, I was on my hands and knees on the floor looking all over for it. At that

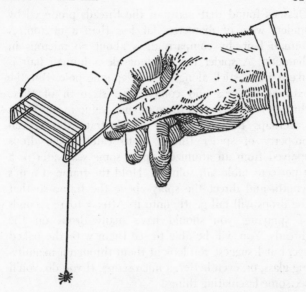

FIG. 20. Collecting spider's thread on frame is easy. Spider lets out thread in an attempt to lower itself to the ground; holder rotates frame to wind up thread.

point, a new secretary entered the room, who was not yet used to the ways of scientists. With a startled look she asked what on earth I was doing. Still on the floor, and peering intently under desks and chairs, I replied, "I'm looking for my spider. It's run away." She said something in a weak, low voice, and fled. At least she could have helped me look for my spider; I never did find it.

Catching the Drops

Take a look at the turns of spider thread on your frame. Can you see them? They may be so fine that you will have to use a strong light and look very closely.

Déssens found that many of the threads produced by spiders were of diameters far less than a micron. A human hair, by comparison, is about 70 microns in diameter. A spider thread alongside a human hair is like a matchstick alongside a telephone pole. But the extreme fineness and comparative strength of these threads is what makes them of such value in our work.

Perhaps the easiest way to illustrate this special property of spider thread is to catch some drops sprayed from an atomizer. Spray some sea water or a 3 per cent table salt solution. Hold the frame at arm's length, and direct the spray above the frame so that the drops will fall gently onto it. After 5 to 10 seconds of spraying, you should have many drops on the threads. You will be able to see them with the naked eye, but I suggest you look at them through a magnifying glass, or, even better, a microscope. If you do, you'll see some fascinating things.

Fig. 21 shows what can be seen through a microscope. If the relative humidity of the air in the room is

Fig. 21. Tiny drops of sea water on spider's thread (*a*) can be seen with magnifying glass or microscope when relative humidity is greater than 70 per cent, but sea-salt particles (*b*) appear in place of drops when humidity falls below 70 per cent.

over 70 per cent (which it may well be in the hot summer months), the drops will be seen as perfect spheres. If, on the other hand, the humidity is less than 70 per cent (which it most likely will be in cold winter months), you will see only what remains of the drop after the water has evaporated—the salt particle.

The appearance of the salt particle will depend on whether you sprayed sea water or a common salt solution. If you used a salt solution the particles will be in the shape of tiny cubes; these are the cubic crystals of sodium chloride. But if you used sea water the particles generally will be anything but cubic. Usually they are very irregular in shape, wrinkled and dried up like a raisin. The explanation is that the sea-salt particle contains far more than just sodium chloride, and no one crystal form appears to gain complete control. Although sodium (Na) and chlorine (Cl) in the form of sodium chloride constitute about three-quarters of the weight of the particle, there are nearly fifty other elements present. The seven most plentiful, after sodium and chlorine, are magnesium (Mg), sulfur (S), calcium (Ca), potassium (K), bromine (Br), carbon (C), and strontium (Sr). Down near the end of the list is the radioactive element radium, but it is present in sea-salt in negligible amounts. About 10^{14} grams of sea-salt would contain only one gram of radium.

It's well worth while to watch the drops on the spider thread change into sea-salt particles or sodium chloride crystals, and then change back into drops. Start your observation with the particles already formed. If they already are in crystal form, fine. If not, hold a light under them. Air in contact with the light bulb will be heated and its relative humidity lowered. As the warm air rises past the drops, particles or crystals will form. Now breathe on them several times. They will absorb water vapor from your breath, grow rapidly, and become large liquid drops. Stop and watch them through the microscope. For a few seconds you will see them getting smaller as the water evaporates. But they are still liquid and spherical; there is no sign of any salt. Then, quite suddenly, you will see the shape of the drop beginning to change, and the salt appears.

The appearance of the salt constitutes the phase change, from liquid to crystal. In the case of sea water the phase change is not a simple one. Although sodium chloride is the first major salt to come out of solution, there are other salts that remain in solution until more water has been evaporated. Magnesium chloride $(MgCl_2)$ is one of them. Thus, the sea-salt particle is really a mixture of solid material (salts that have crystallized) and liquid (which contains the remaining salts and other elements that are in sea water). At almost all relative humidities the particle is partially wet and will stick to a dry object upon impact. And so it was that Woodcock was reasonably certain that sea-salt particles would stick to the glass slide that he exposed from his airplane (Chapter 3).

It would be extremely interesting to use the spider's thread to catch some of the jet drops from a bursting bubble. It is relatively easy to catch them when a great many jet drops are present in the air. The experiments we discussed in Chapter 4 (Figs. 12 and 13) can be used to produce the jet drops. By passing the thread slowly through the cloud of jet drops, you should be able to collect some. After mastering the technique, you could go on to attempt capture of the jet drops from a single bubble. The single-bubble experiment of Fig. 15 or the "flag-in-the-breeze" experiment of Fig. 16 could be utilized. You could check the statement made earlier that the diameter of the top two jet drops is about one-tenth the diameter of the bubble.

Atmospheric scientists have used spider thread in many different studies. In almost all cases, the spider thread was chosen not because it is such a good collector of small drops but because it is an excellent suspension for holding a drop in a fixed position in the air. The gossamer thread interferes very little with the flow of air past the drop, and a drop so suspended is in the next best condition to being free in the air. Air can be blown past at the same speed at which the drop would settle in still air. For all practical purposes, the drop will behave as if it were drifting free.

Charles Keith used this method to find out how fast sea-salt particles would grow by absorbing water vapor from moist air. You will remember, from Chapter 3, that the process of the formation of warm rain requires some extra large cloud drops that will fall faster than the others, will collide and coalesce with them, and grow into raindrops. It was Alfred Woodcock who suggested that the sea-salt particles could be one of the sources of the large cloud drops, and that they would have a head start over the other cloud drops by growing in the humid air beneath the clouds. Well, Keith found out just how fast they would grow. He suspended sea-salt particles of many different sizes on a fine spider thread, and blew air of a known relative humidity past them. Watching the particles through a microscope, he was able to find out exactly how they behaved in moist air. The information he obtained has enabled scientists to compute how large a drop a particular sea-salt particle will be when it enters the base of a cloud. These computations have indicated that the giant sea-salt particles that Woodcock found in the air could very well produce the extra large cloud drops that are needed for the formation of warm rain.

At Night Along the Shore

If you live near the seashore, or have visited it, you surely must have been impressed by the trains of waves that come rolling in to break in the shallow water near the beach. Hissing and foaming, they leave the water white with bubbles as they surge to the shore, and with one final burst of energy spread out into a thin sheet of water that runs far up onto the beach.

If you listen, you can hear the steady hiss made by the multitudes of bubbles as they break. But even if you can't hear the hiss, you may be able to feel what perhaps is best described as a tingling sensation on the side of your face. This is caused by the impact of many tiny drops which have been injected into the air by the bursting bubbles. (Need I add that the wind must be blowing from sea to land for this to occur?) You can feel this same tingling sensation if you hold your face over that glass of ginger ale we discussed in Chapter 5, or over the bubble-filled water as described in the experiment shown in Fig. 12.

As I write, it is late at night, and the wind is howling across the water just outside the laboratory. Peering out through the window, I can see only the blinking of the buoy lights in Woods Hole harbor, and just above the lights the dim orange color of the first quarter moon. Although I cannot see the water, I know it must be covered with breaking waves.

The wind has been blowing all day. This afternoon I drove to a nearby beach on the western side of Cape Cod. The wind was out of the west; in crossing Buzzards Bay it had created many large waves which moved one after the other into the shallow water along the shore. The waves broke, and breakers, bubbles, and foam rolled shoreward. Although I could not see the drops in the air above the breakers, I could feel them. But perhaps now I could return and really see the drops in the air.

Do you find this hard to believe, that one might see the drops easier at night than by day? Let me ask you this: When is it that you can see the tiny dust particles that drift around in the air in a room? Certainly not when the room is ablaze with sunlight streaming into every part of it. It is only when the shades are drawn and the room is dark, and the only strong source of light is a tiny, pencil-like beam of sunlight that is piercing a crack or hole in a shade. Within this beam, surrounded by darkness, the dust particles are easily seen. Similarly, in a forest you will see the pollen and dust not when it is clear and bright roundabout, but only when a shaft of sunlight penetrates the darkness that underlies an umbrella of leaves and branches. Or, how about the entire ocean of air in which we live and in which the clouds grow? The only time you are vividly aware of the dust and haze is when overhanging clouds darken the air and beams of sunlight come streaking through breaks in the overcast.

Along the shore in the darkness of night, we have no beam of sunlight at our disposal. But we do have the beam from a good strong flashlight. In this beam you can easily see the drops that you cannot see in the brightness of the day. Hold the flashlight directly in front of you and project the beam vertically upward. If the wind is coming from the sea, you can look up along the beam and see the haze of drops (Fig. 22). The stronger the surf, the more bubbles are produced, and the more numerous will be the clouds of tiny drops. You will notice that the clouds are sometimes dense, sometimes light, and sometimes you will barely see anything at all. If there are many drops in the air, you may find it of interest to try to collect them on a spider's thread. Some of the drops may have evapo-

FIG. 22. At night along the seashore, flashlight beam clearly reveals clouds of sea-salt particles and droplets of sea water that are not visible by day.

rated enough to become sea-salt particles. But particles or drops, the spider's thread should collect them.

You will find that your flashlight is a very sensitive indicator of drops that have been ejected into the air from the sea. Listen to the waves pounding in; you probably will find that the dense clouds come a few seconds after the largest waves crash against the shore. In the flashlight's beam you are watching nature perform the experiment that we did in the laboratory. (See Chapter 4 and Figs. 12 and 13.)

Look carefully up the beam. You may find that almost all of the drops are in the lowest 2 meters. They have come from the sea just a few meters away, and the wind has not had time to carry them very high into the air. But if you walk away from the shore, you will find that the clouds begin to thin out. They are diluted by mixing with air higher up, and also by the falling out of the larger drops to the ground.

You need not confine this experiment to the edge of the sea. You might try the edge of a lake when waves are breaking. Although I have never done the flashlight experiment along a lake, my guess is that the results would not be as impressive as along the sea. But then, just to see drops or particles in the air you need neither sea nor lake. Try the experiment when it's snowing, raining, or when fog is about. Use your imagination. What you can do with it will surprise you. Just give it a chance.

The Invisible Drops

Now we come to drops I had not intended to write about. In the last chapter I carefully avoided any mention of their existence. I was afraid it would complicate and confuse the issue, and that you might lose interest. But after writing about the clouds of drops that can be seen in a flashlight beam at night along the seashore, I feel they must at least be mentioned.

I have given the impression that all the drops that come from the sea are ejected into the air atop a jet from a bursting bubble (Plate VII). Although this is certainly true for many of the drops, there are some that originate from another part of the bubble. These drops, called film drops, are produced upon the collapse of the film of water that separates the air in the bubble from the air above (Fig. 23). Until that film

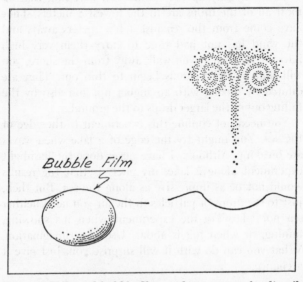

FIG. 23. Collapsed bubble film produces spout of ordinarily invisible droplets when it ruptures. Drops rising on puff of air can be made visible in a special experiment, and they look like the bursting of a Fourth of July rocket.

breaks, the bubble remains quietly at the surface. The breaking of the film triggers a sequence of events that ends with the formation of a jet and the ejection of jet drops. But before the jet can form, the film must collapse, and collapse it does with extreme rapidity. What causes the film to break and how it collapses, are questions that are still being debated. We'll not pursue the various arguments here, but simply accept the fact that many small drops are so produced.

Our experiments at Woods Hole and those of John

Day, at Linfield College, in Oregon, have shown that the larger the bubble, the more film drops are produced. No film drops come from a 0.2 mm diameter bubble, but bubbles larger than 2 mm can produce several hundred.

The amazing thing about these film drops is that the majority of them are too small to be seen, even under a microscope. B. J. Mason, Director-General of the British Meteorological Office, who first detected the film drops, has estimated that they are only a few tenths of a micron across—about the same as the wavelength of light. How can we detect them if we can't see them? We make them grow by condensing water vapor upon them until they can be seen. For this process the air above the water where the bubble breaks must be very free of all other particles, and supersaturated with water vapor. In other words, the relative humidity is greater than 100 per cent, but since the air is free of nuclei there are no particles or drops upon which the water vapor can condense.

When a bubble breaks, the invisible film drops are carried upward in the puff of air from the bubble. And then, right in front of your eyes, you can suddenly see the invisible become visible as the drops grow by water vapor condensation (Fig. 23 and Plate IX). Although I have watched hundreds of bubbles break in this manner, I never cease to admire the delicate beauty that accompanies the appearance of the film drops. As they spring into being, they bring to mind those magnificent rockets that are fired high into the evening sky to end many a Fourth of July celebration. At their zenith they explode into hundreds of pinpoints of light, to grow, and to expand into a twinkling canopy before they fall back to the water.

Although I wish you could see this, I cannot take the space to describe the apparatus that one must use. It is called a diffusion cloud chamber, a device in common use among the nuclear physicists, but first used for meteorological studies by Vincent Schaefer, of the State University of New York.

Though most of the film drops remain unseen in the atmosphere (and you certainly won't see them in your flashlight beam) they are there. When they enter a cloud, they will not provide the giant nuclei necessary for the formation of warm rain, but they will be available to act as nuclei for the cloud drops of average size.

Full Circle

The trail we took up in Chapter 1 has led us into many strange, curious, and exciting places. We began with the raindrops and found out what they are like, how big they are, and how they form and grow in the vast expanse of the clouds. We saw how hygroscopic particles can trigger off warm rain by acting as the nucleus for the formation of a raindrop. In the air over the sea these particles are composed of sea-salt.

Leaving the rain and clouds behind, we went down the trail to the surface of the sea. There we found the origin of the sea-salt particles—air bubbles that are produced in the sea by the breaking of waves. These bubbles come to the surface and break. As the bubble collapses a narrow, pencil-like jet of water rises rapidly from the bottom of the bubble cavity. Small drops of sea water separate from the jet and escape into the atmosphere. Much of the water may evaporate from the drop, leaving the sea-salt behind.

At this point the trail begins to look familiar; the landmarks ahead have been seen before. We have come full circle. Ahead of us the trail turns upward and we can see the salt particles entering the cloud. We can see the raindrops emerging from the cloud to begin their long descent to the earth below.

It is time to leave our trail and pick up another. This is not at all difficult, for the trails of science are many, and they often cross each other. Such is the case with the new trail we are about to explore. We crossed it back in Chapter 4 when we first observed the tiny drops that were ejected into the air by bubbles breaking in a tank of sea water. I did not mention it at the time, but those drops carried an electrical charge. We are going to explore this lead more closely, and in the next two chapters will find out how the sea might influence the flow of electricity that is continually going from the air to the sea.

Chapter 7

SOMETHING ABOUT ELECTRICITY

One day back in 1953, Charles Keith, Alfred Wood-cock, and I were watching air bubbles break at the surface of a small tank of sea water. The bubbles produced a mist of jet drops which hung momentarily in the air before they were carried away on the breeze. Out of idle curiosity one of us took a comb, ran it through his hair to charge it with electricity, and then held it near the bubbling sea water surface. The effect caused by the presence of the charged comb was quite unexpected. All the drops from the jets of the bursting bubbles leaped upward from the water, and with incredible speed flew in long graceful arcs to collision with the comb (Fig. 24). No longer was there any mist in the air. The drops moved so rapidly from water to comb they looked like thin streaks of light.

There was only one explanation to account for the strange behavior of the drops. They were attracted to the comb because each and every one of them carried an electrical charge of sign opposite to that of the charge on the comb. This conclusion followed from one of the basic laws of electricity, which states that like charges repel each other and opposite charges attract. In other words, if the charge on the comb was positive (we had no idea what it was) then the charge on the drops must have been negative. We repeated the experiment several times, with the same result. No doubt about it, the drops were highly charged with electricity.

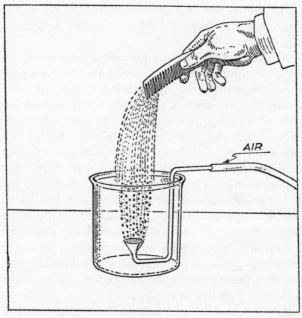

FIG. 24. Electrically charged comb attracts jet drops, which must therefore be carrying a charge opposite in sign to that on the comb.

It suddenly dawned on us that the same thing must be occurring at the surface of the sea. A wave breaks and bubbles are produced. They rise to the surface of the sea, break, and eject electrically charged drops into the air. A large, steady stream of electricity must be rising into the air with the jet drops. We became quite excited. How, we wondered, would this electricity affect what goes on in the atmosphere?

But a few hours later our initial enthusiasm began to dim. A gnawing doubt had come into our minds. Were things really as they appeared to be? Surely, we should check and recheck this new finding. Perhaps we could do the experiment with an object carrying a

charge whose sign was opposite to that of the comb.
Then the jet drops should be repelled instead of
attracted.

At that time we had no equipment with which we
could determine whether a charged object carried positive or negative electricity. (I learned later that when
a hard rubber comb is run through hair it becomes
charged with negative electricity. At least, mine does
in my hair.) But that made no difference. There is a
simple way by which you can charge two objects, one
with positive and the other with negative charge. We
took advantage of another basic law of electricity, the
law of conservation of electric charge. This law, which
was first demonstrated by Benjamin Franklin, states
that electricity can be neither created nor destroyed;
it can only be separated, brought together, or moved
from one point to another. Benjamin Franklin also
gets the credit for the suggestion that electricity be
called either positive or negative.

And so we took two non-conducting objects and
rubbed them together. The rubbing caused the objects
to become charged, but, in doing so, it merely separated
some of the positive and negative charge that was
present in equal amounts in each object. One of the
objects now carried a positive charge, and the other
exactly the same amount of charge, only negative. The
total charge was still zero, just as it was when we had
started the rubbing, for a negative amount added to
the same positive amount gives zero. We had not
created charge, only separated it.

There are many non-conducting objects that can be
rubbed together to separate electricity. You can separate charge by rubbing hard rubber with fur, silk, or
many other cloth materials; you can rub glass with silk,
rubber balloons against dry sweaters or dogs' backs, and
plastic bags on seat covers.

But let's return to those charged jet drops that were

attracted to the charged comb. We had reasoned that they should be repelled by an object with charge opposite to the charge on the comb. Two oppositely charged objects were obtained, as I recall, by rubbing a piece of fur against a hard rubber rod. The rod was held near the jet drops, and they all streaked up to it. We concluded that the rod carried the same sign of charge as had the comb used earlier. Next we held the piece of fur near the jet drops. We expected to see them repelled, for the fur carried a charge of the opposite sign of that of the rod. To our astonishment, just the contrary happened; the drops were attracted to the fur just as they were attracted to the rod or the comb! We tried the experiment over and over and used other charged objects. But nothing changed; the jet drops were attracted to anything as long as it was charged. The sign of the charge appeared to make no difference whatsoever.

The Induced Charge

The evidence was now quite clear. It seemed as if the jet drops were able to sense the charge on the object and get themselves charged with the opposite sign of electricity. In other words, the jet drop charge was being influenced or induced by the presence of the charged object. Well, this type of behavior falls neatly into the realm of what is called charging by induction, or electrostatic induction. I want to explain what this means, because you will run into it time and again in electrical work. Also, we are going to do an experiment in the next chapter that depends upon the principle of induction charging. The explanation is really quite simple. In fact, with our knowledge of how jet drops are formed, plus what we already know about attrac-

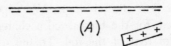

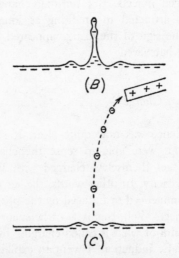

FIG. 25. Electrical attraction between jet drops and charged body can be explained in terms of charging by induction. In (A) positively charged object near water induces negative charge at the surface. When bubble breaks (B) more negative charge is induced on the jet and negatively charged jet drops (C) are attracted to the positively charged object.

tion and repulsion of charges, one might be able to deduce the principle for one's self.

What do you suppose happens when a charged object is held near a water surface where no bubbles are breaking? The situation with a positively charged rod is illustrated in Fig. 25A. The positive charge on the rod attracts the negative charge in the water and repels the positive charge. But the negative charge cannot escape from the water, and so it resides on the surface as a negative layer. And there it would stay, were it not for bubbles.

When a bubble comes to the surface and breaks, a jet of water, we know, rises into the air from the bottom of the collapsing bubble cavity (Plate VII). But in the presence of a positively charged rod, the jet has a negative charge induced on it (Fig. 25B). When the drops pinch off from the jet, they carry this negative charge with them (Fig. 25C). Once free of the water surface they move rapidly toward the charged rod. The closer the rod to the bubble when it breaks, the more heavily charged the drop becomes and the swifter it moves upward to the rod.

If bubbles continue to break in the presence of the charged rod, this process of induction charging of the drops will still go on, but it becomes weaker as each drop strikes the rod. It stops completely when the amount of negative charge carried to the rod by the drops equals the amount of positive charge on the rod. The negative cancels out the positive charge; the charge on the rod becomes zero. The rod ceases to have any inductive effect on jet drop charging.

You must realize that this argument applies equally well if a negatively charged rod is used. The jet drops will still be attracted to the rod, for now a positive charge is induced on them.

I hope you will demonstrate the principle of induction charging to yourself. If you do no other experiment in this book, I urge you to try this one. It is extremely easy to do, and it demonstrates in a very beautiful way one of the most important principles of electrostatics. You can easily produce the bubbles by pouring water from one container into another (Fig. 13). Your charged object can be obtained by—well, I'll leave that up to you. Whatever you use, you'll know, when you hold it near the bursting bubbles, whether it is highly charged.

After Keith, Woodcock, and I had convinced ourselves that it was the charged comb that was really responsible for the highly charged drops, we began to wonder whether the drops might carry a small amount of charge even when the comb was nowhere near them. Might there be some mechanism other than induction by which the jet drops could become charged? We couldn't think of any; in fact, we could think of several reasons why the drops should not carry any charge. But questions are answered only by putting them to the test of experiment, and this question could be answered quickly by an experiment that was not much more complicated than the induction experiment itself. We went ahead with the experiment fully expecting to get negative results, but knowing very well that any positive results could pose some interesting questions concerning the association of jet drops and atmospheric electricity.

Before I tell you what we found out from the experiment, let's give a few minutes to the subject of atmospheric electricity. We'll find out what it is and why so many people are concerned with it.

Atmospheric Electricity

On the first of October in the year 1752, Benjamin Franklin wrote a letter to Peter Collinson in London. He described, in this short letter, an experiment he had done a short time before:

> Make a small cross, of two light strips of cedar; the arms so long, as to reach to the four corners of a large thin handkerchief, when extended: tie the corners of the handkerchief to the extremities of the cross; so you have the body of a kite; which being properly accommodated with a tail, loop, and string, will rise in the air like those made of paper; but this, being of silk, is fitter to bear the wet and wind of a thunder-gust without tearing.

He was describing, as you have no doubt guessed, how he built the kite that he flew when a thunderstorm was overhead. A key was attached to the kite string, and from this key small sparks would "stream out plentifully" when he brought his hand near it (Fig. 26). His kite experiment, one of the best known of all electrical experiments, was a turning point in the study of electricity. Although many clever and ingenious electrical experiments had been done before Franklin's time, they had all dealt with phenomena in the laboratory. Few people suspected (or even gave any thought to) the possibility of a connection between lightning and the electrical sparks they observed in their laboratory experiments. Franklin showed that the small sparks that jumped from the key produced electricity identical with that produced in the laboratory. Lightning, then, was just a giant electrical spark.

Franklin's kite experiment*, and his experiments

* Don't try this experiment; it can be extremely dangerous. In 1753, the year after Franklin flew his kite, a Russian scientist, in

FIG. 26. Ben Franklin's kite lifted his experimentation to a turning point in the study of electricity. Franklin established that the sparks which jumped from the key attached to his kite string in the thunderstorm were no different from electrical effects produced in the laboratory. Lightning is just a giant electric spark.

with sharpened metal points and lightning rods, proved that electricity was far more than something that exists only when rubber or glass rods are rubbed; it is in the air around us. And so began the attempts to penetrate and unravel the mysteries of atmospheric electricity.

For the next 150 years, scientists in many countries studied many aspects of the electrical state of the atmosphere. They made measurements in all seasons of the year and from many positions on the face of the

St. Petersburg, attempting to do a similar type experiment with a sharpened point, was killed when lightning struck the point.

earth. By about 1900 they had established firmly one fact regarding which no one had any doubt. In times of fair weather (which is most of the time) the atmosphere carries a positive charge.

But accompanying this firm fact was a deep mystery. The positive charge was leaking from the atmosphere to the ground at such a rate that the atmosphere should have been completely discharged in about an hour. And yet, in spite of this, the atmosphere never discharged itself. It seemed to be an electrical horn of plenty. How does it recharge itself? Where is its generator? This was the great problem which faced scientists. Some, despairing of ever solving the mystery, believed that the answer would have to await future discoveries of new laws of physics.

Shortly after the turn of the century, however, C. T. R. Wilson, the English physicist who invented the cloud chamber used today for the detection of atomic particles, suggested a way in which the atmosphere might be generating electricity. The generator that keeps charging the atmosphere, he said, is the thunderstorm. Wilson's idea has stood the test of time, and today it is believed that the positive charge of the atmosphere is maintained by an estimated 1000 to 2000 thunderstorms that are in action at any given instant someplace on the face of the globe.

How do the thunderstorms accomplish this? It is generally believed that the upper part of a thunderstorm contains an excess of positive charge while the bottom contains an excess of negative charge (Fig. 27). Lightning and rain cause a transfer of charge between the cloud and the ground, but the major transfer is that of a stream of positively charged ions that moves upward from the ground. The ions are generated at sharp points (tops of trees, houses, blades of grass) by a process known as corona discharge.

In the clear air above the storm the flow of charge

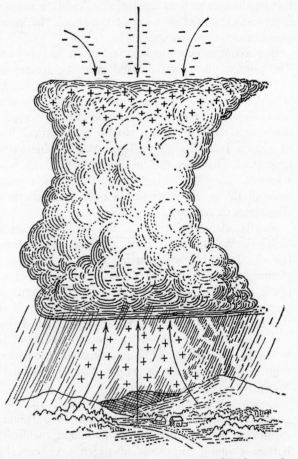

FIG. 27. The thunderstorm is a generator that keeps the upper atmosphere charged with positive electricity. The electrical characteristics of the storm cause negatively charged ions to flow downward into the top of the cloud. A net positive charge is left in the clear air above.

is less complicated. Negatively charged ions are believed to flow downward into the top of the cloud, leaving a net positive charge behind. This positive charge then spreads out to replenish the supply that is continually trickling to the ground in regions of fair weather.

Though most scientists generally agree on these facts, they do not agree on the mechanism that starts and keeps the electrification process going. In the past fifty years a parade of ideas has come and gone. Some of them, in one form or another, state that the electrification arises only after rain, snow, or hail is formed in the cloud. In other words, the precipitation makes the electricity. This is the prevailing view among most scientists today. But a few of them, particularly Bernard Vonnegut, of the State University of New York at Albany, believe it is the other way around—that the electrification comes first and that it may in fact help the rain to form. These opposing views have caused a flurry of activity in problems of thunderstorm electrification, and out of this exciting and healthy controversy some answers and new problems are bound to come.

Although thunderstorm electrification is being studied actively, it is by no means at the center of the stage. Other scientists, particularly those who are studying the electrification of clouds which do *not* develop into thunderstorms, share the spotlight. These studies are very important, for they seek to discover whether charged cloud drops increase (or decrease) the collection efficiency.*

The electrical state of the free atmosphere (no clouds, rain, or thunderstorms) has always received much attention. How is the charge carried in clear air?

* You may recall from Chapter 3 that the collection efficiency of a large drop is that fraction of the small drops directly in its path that it sweeps up and collects as it falls.

How good a conductor is the air? Does it vary? And why? How does the potential or voltage change with height? The list of questions is nearly endless.

The charge in clear air resides on a variety of carriers, ranging in size from ions to giant particles, like the sea-salt particles. Air is a relatively poor conductor of electricity near the surface of the earth but a very good one at high levels. Up there the air is clean, and cosmic rays, in colliding with air molecules, create great numbers of ions.

But the most obvious fact about the atmosphere in fair weather is that the potential or voltage increases with height. Do you understand just what is meant by reference to the potential of a point in space? No doubt you would not be too puzzled if I said that the potential of a particular wire or a battery terminal was 100 volts. But perhaps I am straining your concept of electricity too far when I speak of the potential at a point in the atmosphere, where there is no wire or battery—just air. The only way of explaining this in a few words is to give the basic definition of potential. The potential of any point (whether on a wire, a battery, or in space) is a measure of the work done against electrical forces when a positive charge is moved from the zero reference level (usually the ground) to the point in question. Read that sentence a few times and see whether you grasp its meaning. Notice that it says nothing about electrical currents. You must understand that electrical currents (measured in amperes) have nothing to do with voltage. Current is a measure of the flow of charge; voltage is a measure of the force which causes it to flow. The atmosphere carries a positive charge, and it would repel any positive charge that we tried to move up into it from the ground. We would have to do work against this electrical force to push a positive charge upward. The higher we went with it the more work we'd have to do. And this, according to the definition of voltage or potential simply means that a voltage exists and that it is increasing with height.

At the ground the potential, by definition, is zero. At a height of one meter it is about 130 volts positive. As you walk around out-of-doors your head is at a level in the air where the potential is about 200 volts higher than the ground you walk on! You're not aware of this at all; you're not going to receive any shock because the currents that flow in the atmosphere are extremely small. The potential of 130 volts at a height of one meter drives a positive current downward to the ground, but this current is only about 10^{-12} ampere (one millionth of one millionth of an ampere) per square meter. You can't begin to detect this, but there are instruments that can.

Although near the ground the potential of the atmosphere increases at a rate of about 130 volts per meter of altitude (the change in potential per meter is called the potential gradient), the potential gradient diminishes the higher up we go. At a height of about 10 kilometers it is barely a few volts per meter. Nevertheless, at these altitudes the total potential of the atmosphere attains the astonishing value of about 300,000 volts above ground!

We must conclude this all-too-brief account of atmospheric electricity, but I hope you keep the following facts in mind. The atmosphere carries a net positive charge. This charge, leaking down to the ground all over the world, creates a current of about 1500 amperes. Thunderstorms are thought to be the main source of replenishment of the atmospheric charge, but the mechanism by which this happens is still not clear.

Chapter 8

ELECTRICITY FROM THE SEA

You will recall that charging of jet drops by induction will occur whenever a charged object is held near a bursting bubble (Fig. 25). But what if the charged object is not there? Does the jet drop still carry a charge?

The experiment that gave the answer was done in the following way. A metal plate, about 10 by 10 cm and with a hole of about 1 mm diameter in the center, was placed horizontally over the water and about 1 cm above it. When the hole was placed directly over the spot where the bubbles broke, the jet drops flew up through the hole and into the air above (Fig. 28). The purpose of the metal plate was to shield the bubble jet from the influence of any charged object that was held above the plate. The jet drops would then be free from charging by induction.

But if the drops carried a charge obtained in some other way, this charge could be detected when the drops passed up through the hole and into the presence of a charged object. A test was carried out by rubbing two objects together to electrify them, and then holding one (a rod) above the plate and near the spot where the top jet drops were being ejected. Before the rod was held there, the drops were rising vertically and falling back along the same path. But in the presence of the charged rod, the drops were deflected slightly toward it. Clearly, the drops carried electric charge!

The final test was to see how the drops behaved in

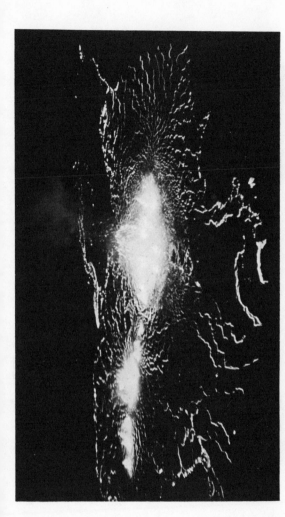

PLATE X. Kilauea volcano in Hawaii erupts, in June 1952. View is of the fire pit of Halemaumau. Circular area in center is at least 200 feet across.

PLATE XI. Steam clouds rise where molten lava from Kilauea's 1960 eruption flows into sea. Clouds hold high concentration of sea-salt particles. (Photo by Jack Pales)

PLATE XII. Lightning in the volcano cloud over Surtsey, Iceland, in the evening of December 1, 1963. The picture was made with a 90-second time exposure. The height of the top of the picture (over Surtsey) is estimated to be about 5 miles. The lightning probably originated from a thunderstorm which was initiated by the volcanic eruption. (Photo by Sigurgeir Jónasson)

PLATE XIII. Beginning of an explosion in Surtsey's crater. The spear-shaped plumes of ash, sea water, and cloud hurtled upward at speeds of up to 200 miles per hour.

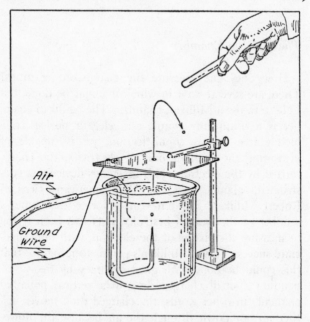

FIG. 28. Experiment to detect non-induced charge on jet drop is illustrated here. Metal plate above jar shields drops from induced charging. Drops rise and fall on vertical path through hole in plate until charged object approaches. Drops then are deflected from vertical path.

the presence of the other charged object. One would expect them to be repelled. And they were! This simple experiment with the equal but oppositely charged objects proved that the jet drops carried a charge that was obtained by some process other than induction.

After this experiment others were carried out to determine exactly how much charge was carried by jet drops. We reasoned that if the charge on the jet drops was large enough, then perhaps the total charge carried into the air by all the jet drops from the sea might be of importance in atmospheric electricity.

The Millikan Chamber

How does one measure the charge on jet drops? There are several ways in which it might be done, but I chose to use a Millikan chamber. The Millikan chamber is a beautifully simple and elegant device, completely free of any sophistication, yet is capable of measuring the smallest unit of electricity, the charge carried by the electron. This ingenious device was constructed, about 1910, by the American physicist Robert Millikan. For ten years prior to that time, a number of the world's best physicists had been trying to measure the charge of the electron, with only moderate success. It was Millikan's genius to recognize that this could be done with great accuracy by freely suspending a small charged drop in a vertical potential gradient. In other words, the charged drop moves neither up nor down through the air because the downward pull of gravity is exactly balanced by the upward pull of the electrical force. Millikan suspended his charged drops (he used oil drops sprayed from an atomizer: oil does not evaporate as fast as water does) in the center of a chamber whose top and bottom consisted of metal plates. A battery was connected between the two plates, the negative side to the upper plate if the drop carried a positive charge (Fig. 29). The battery connection was made in such a way that the voltage between the plates could be varied. This control enabled Millikan to provide exactly that value of upward electrical pull to just balance the force of gravity. The principle of the Millikan chamber is analogous to that of the vertical wind tunnel we discussed back in Chapter 2 (Fig. 5). Both suspend drops against the pull of gravity, one by electrical forces and the other by the forces generated by moving air.

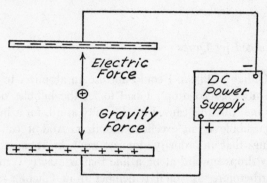

FIG. 29. Schematic diagram illustrates principle of Millikan experiment. When electric force upward on charged oil drop exactly balances downward force of gravity, drop remains stationary in chamber.

You can easily demonstrate to yourself the principle of the Millikan chamber. Use a charged comb and try the induction charge experiment shown in Fig. 25. But this time, slowly lift the comb when you see the drops streaking toward it. The drops will rise slower and slower until, finally, they cease to rise at all, and momentarily some will hover in air. At that moment, the pull of gravity is just balanced by the electrical attraction of the induced charge for the comb.

I shall go no further with a description of the Millikan chamber. This is not the place to describe the incredible refinements and calculations that Millikan carried out to determine the charge carried by an electron. I only want you to understand the basic principle behind his wonderful device—the suspending of a charged drop in a potential gradient. For his painstaking work, Millikan, in 1923, received the Nobel prize in physics.

Charged Jet Drops

Unlike Millikan, I could not use an atomizer to create my charged drops; I had to let the bubbles do it
for me. But this caused no difficulty at all, for a bursting bubble is an excellent atomizer. And it can do
things that an ordinary atomizer can't do. It can shoot
tiny drops upward along a line that is exactly vertical.
Furthermore, as you'll remember from Chapter 5, if
the bubble size does not change, the drops will rise to
precisely the same height (Fig. 17).

I took advantage of the marksmanship of the bubble
and used a Millikan chamber that had a tiny hole in
the center of the bottom plate (Fig. 30). The chamber
was placed above the water, in just the right position
for the top jet drop streaking upward from the burst
bubble to pass through the hole in the bottom plate
and reach its maximum height at a point about halfway
between the two plates. An instant later it would fall
back through the hole and down to the water.

Getting the hole directly over the bubble was not
too difficult, for Ted Spencer, who had built this very
fine Millikan chamber, had attached to it some manual
gear drives. With the aid of these gears we could move
the chamber with great precision in any direction in
the horizontal plane. When the chamber was at the
proper height, I would look underneath to see how far
the hole had to be moved to receive the drops. Usually
it was not more than 4 or 5 mm. A strong beam of light
would reveal the tiniest drops when they collided and
stuck to the bottom plate. It was then a relatively
simple matter to move the chamber in the proper direction and watch the line of drops from successive
bubbles march across the underside of the plate until,

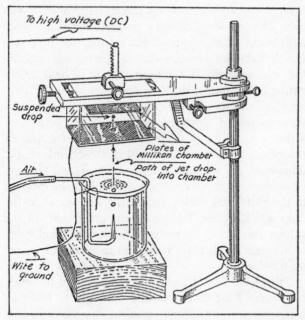

To high voltage (DC)

Suspended drop

Air

Plates of Millikan chamber

Path of jet drop into chamber

Wire to ground

FIG. 30. Millikan chamber can be adapted as in this illustration for measurement of the positive electric charge on the jet drops. Apparatus is swiveled to bring hole in bottom of chamber in line with path of jet drops.

finally, they passed through the hole and into the chamber.

A direct current power supply was used to put on the upper plate (and on no other part of the apparatus) any value of voltage, plus or minus, up to a maximum of 12,000 volts.* The bottom plate was always connected to an electrical ground, as was the sea water. I soon found that only with a negative voltage on the upper plate could the charged drops be sus-

* As high voltage is involved in the operation of this chamber the experiment can be dangerous. It is not recommended that the reader attempt to build this apparatus.

pended when they came up through the hole. It was
clear that the drops carried a positive charge. By quick
adjustment of the value of the voltage, the drop was
exactly balanced between the two plates, moving neither up nor down. In the narrow beam of light illumi-
nating the chamber, the drop appeared like the bright-
est star hung in a midnight sky. For perhaps two or
three seconds it remained that way. Then, because of
a slow evaporation of water from the drop (in spite of
our efforts to keep the air moist in the chamber), the
downward gravitational force weakened and the upward electrical force took over and pulled the drop up
to the plate. But during those brief seconds when the
drop was balanced, I obtained the exact value of the
voltage on the upper plate. This was the vital piece
of information that was needed to calculate the charge
on the drop.

I think we should look at this calculation in detail,
for shortly I am going to show you how to build an
extremely simple Millikan chamber. You won't be able
to use it to do quite what you could do with the chamber shown in Fig. 30, but you will be able to perform
some interesting experiments on jet drop induction
charging. And you'll need the equation we're about
to derive to compute the charge carried by the drops.

At the moment of balance, the gravitational force
(F_g) on the drop must just equal the electrical force
(F_E). Thus we can write the simple equation:

$$(1) \qquad F_g = F_E$$

This equality, by itself, is of little help, but we can
substitute for each of the terms an expression that we
can work with. The gravitational force (F_g) on any
body is the product of the mass (m) of that body
times the acceleration caused by gravity (g). In alge-
braic shorthand, $F_g = m \times g$. We can break this down
even further, for the mass of a body is its volume times

its density (D). And so, for our spherical drops we have

$$F_g = \frac{4}{3} \times \pi \times R^3 \times D \times g$$

where R is the drop radius. Let's now look at the right-hand side of equation (1). The electrical force (F_E) on the drop is the product of the charge (Q) and the potential gradient, which, in turn is the voltage (V) between the plates divided by the distance (S) that separates them. Thus $F_E = Q \times \dfrac{V}{S}$. Now we can go back to equation (1) and substitute our new expressions for F_g and F_E to get $\dfrac{4}{3} \times \pi \times R^3 \times D \times g = Q \times \dfrac{V}{S}$ and, by solving for Q, we get

$$(2) \qquad Q = \frac{4 \times \pi \times R^3 \times D \times g \times S}{3 \times V}$$

This is the equation that I used to compute the charge on the jet drops. The charge (Q) was quickly obtained by substituting for R, D, g, S, and V. The voltage (V) was known, and the distance between the plates (S) was easily measured. The gravitational acceleration is the same for all bodies and is about 980 cm/s². The density of the drop is 1 g/cm³ for fresh water and about 1.02 g/cm³ for sea water. But how does one obtain the drop radius (R)? Do you remember (back in Chapter 5) that I pointed out that Charles Keith had found the size of the jet drop and its ejection height as a function of the bubble size? All one has to do is to measure the height to which the top jet drop is ejected, and then, with a graph, obtain the radius (R) of the jet drop (Fig. 31).

A final word of caution is very much in order to those of you who attempt to use equation (2). You must use the proper units when substituting numbers for R, D, etc. Should R be expressed in microns, centimeters, inches, or miles? What kinds of units should

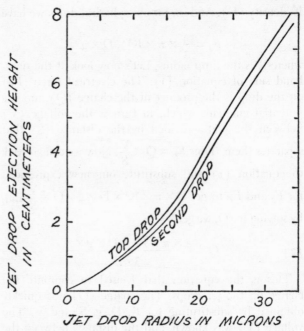

FIG. 31. The radius of a jet drop (in microns) can be read directly from this graph when the ejection height of the drop has been measured.

be used? Well, I'm not going to discuss the various systems of units common in science. I am simply going to rewrite equation (2) in such a way that you can compute the charge (Q) directly in terms of the number of electron charges carried by the drop. Remember, the electron carries a single unit of charge, the smallest unit of electricity known. This charge is sometimes called an elementary charge.

If the distance between the plates (S) is measured in centimeters, if R is measured in microns, and V in volts, then the charge, expressed in elementary charges, is

$$(3) \qquad Q = 2.6 \times 10^3 \times \frac{S \times R^3}{V}$$

This equation is very convenient, and the drop charge can be calculated very rapidly. For example, suppose that a jet drop of radius 10 microns is just balanced when a negative potential of 10,000 volts is on the upper plate. And suppose further that the plates are one centimeter apart. We can see immediately from equation (3) that the drop charge is $Q = 2.6 \times 10^3 \times \frac{1 \times 10^3}{10^4} = 260$ elementary charges. In other words, the drop carries a positive charge that is 260 times larger than the charge carried by an electron.

Many jet drop charge experiments were performed with the Millikan chamber. Experiments were carried out with bubbles both large and small, and with bubbles produced by capillary tips and in the splashing of sea water. Bubbles were allowed to break in water at room temperature and in water whose temperature was just a bit above freezing. Even the age of the bubble was varied; short-lived bubbles were produced from tips within a centimeter of the water surface; other bubbles took many seconds to rise to the surface from tips that were more than 30 cm below. In all the experiments I was trying to cover the range of bubble size, age, and water temperature that might be expected when whitecaps form on the open sea.

The experiments showed that the jet drops carried positive electricity in amounts that varied from about one hundred to several thousand elementary charges. The larger the drop and the older the bubble, the larger was the charge. Jet drops from bubbles breaking in cold water carried more charge than those from bubbles in warm water. The top jet drop carried at least twice as much charge as the second drop.

Why are the jet drops charged? That's an excellent

question to which I have no adequate answer. Only an idea or a hunch. I suspect that the key to the solution will be found in the electrical double layer. This double layer, which is found at the surface of many liquids, consists of two thin, oppositely charged layers that are sandwiched together within a micron of the surface. Perhaps the bubble jet has found a way to shear off the positively charged layer and inject a part of it into the jet drops. Although the negative layer is less than a micron away, the incredible acceleration and speed of the jet may be able to accomplish this feat in much the same way that a sudden jerk on a tablecloth can snatch it off the table, leaving the dishes behind.

There is a general conclusion that could be drawn from all these experiments: It is probable that whenever bubbles break at the surface of the sea, they eject positively charged drops into the atmosphere. The sea, like the thunderstorm, may be helping to maintain the positive charge of the atmosphere. But before we go into our concluding remarks on jet drops and atmospheric electricity, let's take a look at that Millikan chamber I said you could build quite easily.

A Homemade Millikan Chamber

When I discussed the principle of the Millikan chamber, I suggested that you demonstrate it to yourself by holding a charged rod just the proper distance above a bursting bubble so that you not only charge the top jet drop by induction but also momentarily suspend it. This is the simplest Millikan chamber imaginable, for if the potential gradient was known at the point where the drop was suspended, the charge on the drop could be computed. Although it is possible to compute this potential gradient, it is a bit awkward, and I will not describe the method here. Besides, I have something else in mind that I think will be more interesting.

The essential ingredients of a Millikan chamber are the plates and a DC power supply. To suspend the naturally-charged jet drops you would need a power supply that will deliver several thousand volts. I definitely do not recommend this; it would be expensive and extremely dangerous. Rather, I suggest that a large charge be induced on the jet drops; then they could be suspended quite easily in potential gradients provided by small DC batteries. But even here, under certain conditions, the batteries could be a source of danger. I suggest that the experiment described below be done either by an adult or under adult supervision.

The charge can be induced on the jet drops by connecting a battery between the water and a plate that is placed horizontally above the water where the bubbles are breaking. To be on the safe side connect a carbon resistor of about a million ohms resistance (they cost less than fifty cents) to one of the terminals of the battery (see Fig. 32). Then you won't receive a shock if by accident you happen to touch both plate and water at the same time. Don't use a metal plate with a single hole in it; you might become frustrated in trying to get the jet drops through the hole. Get yourself a piece of ordinary metal window screening (which has more holes than wire), and the drops will pass through quite easily. The screening need not be more than about 4 cm on a side, and can be placed a centimeter or less above the water (Fig. 32).

If the top jet drop, after passing through the screen, does not rise much higher, you can get double duty out of the screen, using it also as the lower plate of the two parallel plates between which the drop is to be suspended. Place a second plate (this need not be a screen) at a height just above that attained by the top jet drop. Connect a second battery between the

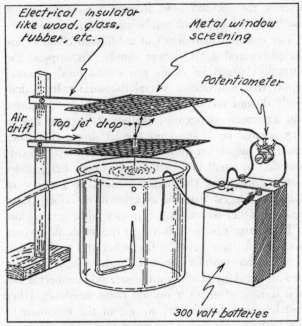

FIG. 32. Homemade Millikan chamber suspends charged jet drops between two squares of window screen in a potential gradient established by a small DC battery. Charge on the jet drops is induced by a second battery which provides a potential difference of 300 volts between water and lower screen.

two plates and you'll be able to suspend the drops. That's it. Your Millikan chamber is finished. You have created two potential gradients, one to induce a large charge on the drops, and the other to suspend them.

Let me say a few words about the batteries and the magnitude of the charges that you can induce on the drops. I recommend that you use 300-volt industrial batteries; they are small, weigh only about a pound, and can be obtained at a radio or television store. Unfortunately, they are expensive, costing about $9 apiece. A potentiometer (which only costs about $2) connected across the battery between the plates will enable you to vary the voltage on the top plate to get just that value required to suspend the drop. The potentiometer resistance should be at least one million ohms. After the batteries have been wired up, it would be a good idea, for safety's sake, to cover the battery terminals with electrical or some other type of insulating tape.

Consider an example of what this Millikan chamber can do. Suppose you have bubbles that are ejecting the top jet drop to a height of 2 cm. And suppose further that you have the lower screen just 0.5 cm above the water. The potential gradient, inducing the charge, then, will be 600 volts per centimeter. Now I happen to know from my own experiments that the induced charge is about 60,000 elementary charges for a top drop of this size and about three times that for the second drop. So what voltage do we need on the upper plate for drop suspension if the plates are 2 cm apart? You'll find out by using equation (3), substituting 60,-000 for Q, 2 for S, and 14 (Fig. 31) for R, and solving for the voltage (V). If I've done it correctly, V is about 230 volts.

Notice in Fig. 32 that when the top drop is balanced, it drifts horizontally (from drafts in the room) for only a short distance, and then rises upward to the plate. This movement is a result of evaporation. The second drop, however, is never balanced but rises immediately to the plate. The plate voltage would have to be decreased to balance this drop.

Although this experiment is crude, it demonstrates, in a relatively simple way, a very powerful method for measuring extremely small amounts of electricity on tiny drops. Millikan's technique has been used by many scientists, and its utility in measuring the charge on jet drops from sea water is only one of the numerous ways in which it has benefited science.

Electricity from the Sea

When the winds at sea are light, the surface of the water will be rippled. Small waves will be seen, but no whitecaps will appear. In regions of high winds and storms whitecaps may cover more than 10 per cent of the surface of the sea. But on the average only between 3 and 4 per cent of the ocean area of the world is covered with whitecaps. Still, the sum total of this foam- and bubble-producing area is impressive. It covers an expanse of sea that is about 1.3 times the area of the United States. At least twenty or thirty bubbles are estimated to be breaking every second on each square centimeter of this surface. Even without calculating it, you can imagine what a fantastic number of jet drops are being hurled upward every second from the oceans of the world. And if each of these drops carries a positive charge, then a current of positive electricity is rising from the sea to the air.

Many, perhaps most, of the jet drops will not escape the clutches of gravity for more than a few seconds, and will return to the sea with their electrical charge. These drops cannot influence the electrical state of the atmosphere. But other smaller drops, as we saw in the last two chapters, are carried high into the atmosphere and may spend hours or days before they, too, return to the sea. Any charge that they carry can and will influence the electrical state of the atmosphere.

Is this influence of any significance? It may be. Calculations I have made indicate that the amount of charge carried up into the air every second from the oceans of the world constitutes an electrical current of about 150 amperes. Compared to the currents that surge through the electrical appliances in an average house, this is not an overwhelmingly impressive figure. The fuse box in my house is rated at 100 amperes, and that much current, I think, would flow through the house if I were to turn on every electrical appliance—including the automatic can opener that never did work properly. But compared to the thunderstorm, the main source of electrical current in the atmosphere, this amount is a respectable figure. The average thunderstorm generates a current of only about one ampere; the approximately 1500 amperes of positive current that has been found to flow continuously from the atmosphere to the earth presumably is generated by a total of about 1500 thunderstorms. You will recall from the last chapter that this is believed to be about the number of thunderstorms that are in action at any given time on the face of the globe.

The electrical current generated by the sea has been estimated to be about the same as that generated by 150 thunderstorms. This is small, being only about 10 per cent of all the current that is generated in the atmosphere, but it could be of some significance. It may help to provide a space charge which could perhaps influence the growth and development of clouds and the formation of rain. The manner in which electrical charges might do this is not yet completely understood, but at present it is an area of research that is being given a lot of attention.

Let me conclude this section on a note of caution. These ideas concerning charge from the sea have been presented in a manner that is perhaps too assured and too matter-of-fact. One is almost bound to leave such impressions when one is forced to present a complex train of ideas in relatively few pages. Were I to state every assumption, every guess, and, yes, perhaps even the wishful thinking that went into each statement, I would have to write a book longer than this one. So let me say as clearly as I can that many assumptions went into the calculation of the flow of charge from the sea. Although the calculations were based on what are believed to be good experimental facts, these facts, for the most part, were obtained in the laboratory. And the facts that one discovers in the laboratory must be examined closely before they are cited to explain phenomena in the out-of-doors.

With this caution in mind, we have made measurements of space charge along the shore of the sea. I believe they provide evidence that positively charged jet drops are rising from the sea. But this evidence is not enough. A single set of measurements can point to the truth but will not necessarily uncover it. Truth is much more elusive than that. The measurements will have to be taken again and again, not only by us at Woods Hole but by other scientists in other parts of the world. Until they are taken, we cannot be certain that the idea of charge coming from the sea is a solid fact and not just an interesting but erroneous idea.

Surface Films, Jet Drop Charge, and Size

At the beginning of Chapter 4, I said that the surface of the sea is a vast land of two dimensions, whose properties can be quite different from those of the air above or the water beneath. One of these properties is the chemical nature of the surface. It is known that portions of the surface of the sea can become covered with a very thin film of organic material that presumably comes from the organisms living in the sea. I do not exaggerate when I say very thin.

The thickness of these films is measured in terms of the length of its molecules; this is only about 0.01 micron. Nevertheless, a film that is one molecule in thickness is relatively thick for any land of two dimensions.

Most of the film molecules are longer than they are wide, and they rest side by side on the surface of the water. Like a bunch of matchsticks, they stack themselves vertically when horizontal surface pressures (Fig. 33a) squeeze them together. The film now has its maximum thickness (the length of the molecule), and will profoundly affect what goes on at the surface. Although you cannot see these compressed films on the sea, you can see how they destroy or damp out the small waves. The surface of the water appears smooth and glassy, and it is said to be covered with a slick. In harbors or near the shore man-made slicks are very common.

If the surface pressure is released, the compressed film expands and the molecules slump over, lying nearly horizontal on the surface (Fig. 33b). This is as thin

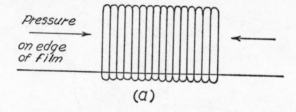

Pressure
on edge
of film

(a)

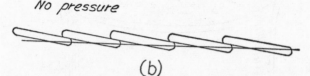

No pressure

(b)

FIG. 33. Surface film molecules are represented in (a) as stacked vertically under squeezing of horizontal surface pressures and in (b) as slumped when pressures are released. It is apparent that thickness of film depends on compression of molecules.

as the film can get, the thickness being perhaps only a tenth of what it was when compressed. These expanded films will not cause slicks to appear, but they can affect what goes on at the surface.

The point I want to make about these films is that, irrespective of their being thick or thin, compressed or expanded, they may have a strong influence in determining whether a jet drop carries a positive charge, a negative charge, or no charge at all. In laboratory experiments bubbles breaking at a clean sea water surface will produce positively charged jet drops. If a finger is touched to the surface, the bubbles generally will

FIG. 34. Film of body oil from fingertip spreads over surface changing charge on jet drops from positive to negative. Spreading of invisible film is revealed in movements of specks of dust on surface.

start producing negatively charged drops. A film of natural body oil has spread out on the surface of the water (Fig. 34) and somehow interfered with the bubbles' charge-producing mechanism.

These films affect not only the charge but also the size of the drop. If you repeat some of the experiments of Chapters 4 and 5 with a film on the surface of the water, you will see what I mean. Try other oils to produce the film; both castor oil and olive oil produce excellent films. Films are just as easy to remove from the surface as they are to apply. Holding it by the edge, place a clean paper towel on the surface. Then lift it off when water has soaked into it. Do this three or four times and the surface will be free of film.

There is not much more I can say about films and their influence on jet drops, largely because there is so much that we have yet to learn. Although studies show that films can influence many things that happen at a water surface in the laboratory, we don't know just how much importance this has for events that go on at the surface of the sea. We have yet to find out just what percentage of the sea actually is covered with an organic film. But I will venture to guess that not many years will go by before we do find out. Many scientists are becoming interested in the surface of the sea and the curious things that occur there. The land of two dimensions is about to be explored thoroughly.

Chapter 9

VOLCANOES, SEA WATER, AND
ELECTRICITY

There are few signposts along the research trail. You must find your way through the new land as best you can. Your compass is reason, perseverance, and, most important of all, the continual questioning of nature. Your map is a chart of the trails of those who have gone that way before.

Your trail seldom coincides exactly with any of those of past adventurers, but often you will find you are about to cross the track of one who had been there many years ago. And though the trail is overgrown with the weeds and bushes of time, do not ignore it. Beneath those bushes may lie a signpost whose directions, combined with those obtained from your own compass, might lead you to unknown mountains and hidden valleys.

In this chapter we are going to see how the discovery of some of these signposts has led from bubbles in the sea and sea-salt particles to volcanoes in the sea. We will take a brief trip down one or two of the old trails. Though the trip may be difficult, the information on the signposts and the sights along the trail will make the trip well worthwhile.

Kilauea Erupts

In the latter part of June of 1952, Alfred Woodcock and I were on the island of Hawaii investigating airborne sea-salt particles and rainfall (Chapter 3). One of the roads on which we collected raindrops and rain-water led up through the rain forests and into the clouds. At the highest point on this road, 4000 feet up the flank of Mauna Loa volcano, was Kilauea (Kee-lau-ã-ah) volcano.

Kilauea is one of the largest and most famous of the world's active volcanoes, and its magnificence and grandeur will never be forgotten by those who have had the good fortune to see it. The size of the crater overwhelms the imagination. Mark Twain, who visited Kilauea a hundred years ago, said of it, ". . . here was a vast, perpendicular, walled cellar, nine hundred feet deep in some places, thirteen hundred in others, level floored, and *ten miles in circumference!* Here was a yawning pit upon whose floor the armies of Russia could camp, and have room to spare."*

The Russian armies would have to watch their step, for on the floor of this vast crater, like a crater within a crater, is the "fire pit" of Halemaumau (Ha-lay-mau-mau, the House of Everlasting Fire). Halemaumau is a giant circular pit, over two thousand feet in diameter, whose walls drop almost vertically about a thousand feet to a lake of lava. In the last century this lake was almost continuously a seething inferno of molten rock, but in October of 1934 its periodic eruptions ceased. The lava lake became cold, quiet, and frozen over.

Just before midnight on the twenty-seventh of June 1952, after a slumber of nearly eighteen years, Hale-maumau awoke. Gigantic fountains of molten lava broke through the frozen crust and sprayed nearly 1000 feet into the air. Within a day the entire surface of the lava lake was asplash with liquid rock at a temperature of about 2000 degrees Fahrenheit!

The eruption signaled the start of a parade of people

* See Volume II of Twain's *Roughing It.*

up the road to Kilauea. In Hawaii a volcano in eruption is relatively safe to approach, and people run to and not away from it. On the second night of the eruption, Woodcock and I were among those who were streaming up the road for a nighttime view of a volcano in action. If a view in the daytime is interesting, then how much more so it is at night, for then the red-hot lava fountains are vividly etched against the inky darkness.

The last half mile to the edge of the fire pit was by foot over the lava of some previous eruption on the floor of Kilauea. Although we could not see the lava lake as we began our final approach, the smoke clouds that rose from the pit reflected a flickering crimson glow, as if a giant forge lay underneath. When we reached the edge and were able to see into the pit, we immediately became aware of the incredible beauty and brute power of a volcanic eruption (Plate X). In the center of that lake a line of fountains sprayed liquid, red-hot lava several hundred feet into the air. When the lava plummeted back to the lake, it set up waves that rolled outward to the edge of the pit. They moved into regions where the lava had cooled and had a dark, crusted surface. Cracks appeared in the crust, and long jagged streaks of light cut into the night from the still red-hot lava beneath. Again, in the words of Mark Twain, "It looked like a colossal railroad map of the State of Massachusetts done in chain lightning on a midnight sky. Imagine it—imagine a coal-black sky shivered into a tangled network of angry fire!"

We returned to Woods Hole with far more than just information on raindrops and sea-salt nuclei. We had witnessed a volcanic eruption and although we couldn't see any way in which volcanoes fitted into our work on rain and the surface of the sea, we could not forget the spectacle. Memories of the eruption were indelibly imprinted on our minds.

Steam Clouds from the Sea

Occasionally lava from an eruption of Mauna Loa or from one of the numerous craters of Kilauea will flow many miles down the flanks of the volcano and into the sea. From the point of contact of the intensely hot lava with the sea billowing steam clouds mushroom high into the air (Plate XI). We might expect these clouds to be ordinary steam clouds, formed by condensation of the water vapor that had been evaporated rapidly from the sea by the hot lava. They should be comparable to the steam clouds that are produced from the spout of a teakettle simmering on the back of a stove. In other words, these steam clouds should be nothing more than a collection of tiny droplets of distilled water.

But are they? Woodcock was talking one day to a person who had seen the steam clouds produced when lava from Mauna Loa had gone into the sea. This person dropped the remark that the paint on cars driven near these steam clouds was spotted in a very curious way. In this remark was a signpost, a clue that the clouds contained more than just water. Surely, clouds of distilled water droplets would do no more than make a car wet. Could there have been some sea-salt particles in those clouds?

The best way to answer the question was to fly through one of the steam clouds and find out. In 1960, lava from an eruption of Kilauea made its way to the sea and produced steam clouds in great profusion. Woodcock went to Hawaii, flew into these clouds, and collected some of the cloud particles on small glass slides in the same way that he sampled sea-salt particles in the clear air (Chapter 3). When he examined these slides under a microscope, he found sea-salt particles

in numbers the likes of which he had never found before. The concentration of sea-salt particles far ex-
ceeded that which he had found in hurricanes, where
the entire surface of the sea was pumping sea-salt particles into the air. It was quite clear that the splashing
of sea water onto hot lava did more than just evaporate water; it was a very potent source of sea-salt particles.

Woodcock reasoned that if the production of such
large numbers of sea-salt particles is just a simple matter of having sea water come into contact with molten
lava, then we ought to be able to simulate the process
in the laboratory. Perhaps we could make our own volcano and reproduce what nature appears to be doing.

Woodcock and Spencer did the experiment. They
took a chunk of Hawaiian lava and heated the upper
part with an oxy-acetylene torch until they had produced a puddle of molten rock. And then, without a
moment's delay, they squirted sea water onto the hot
lava, and—presto!—they had an instant do-it-yourself
home volcano. There was a sudden sizzling and
explosive-like sound, and a cloud rose from the hot
surface (Fig. 35). They let the cloud rise through an
open-ended cardboard cylinder, and trapped a part of
it by suddenly placing covers on each end. The cylinder
was then set aside for several hours. The cloud particles
settled slowly in the air, and fell onto clean glass slides
that had been placed on the inside of the bottom cover.

When examined under the microscope, these slides
were found to be covered with thousands of tiny sea-
salt particles, just like the ones that had been collected
in the real volcanic cloud. From this type of laboratory
experiment Woodcock and Spencer were able to show
that sea water striking molten lava produced sea-salt
particles at the almost unbelievable rate of about 100
million per square centimeter per second. This is tens

PLATE XIV. Recording the potential gradient as Surtsey's eruption clouds billow upward to heights of over 1000 feet. The horizontal antenna that measured the potential gradient from the fishing boat *Haraldur* can be seen in the upper left-hand corner of the photograph.

PLATE XV. Spinning smoke ring in Surtsey's eruption cloud.

PLATE XVI. Three streams of lava flowing off Surtsey and into the sea on April 24, 1964. Note the steaming of the sea around the base of each of the three cloud plumes. (Photo by Gardar Pálsson)

PLATE XVII. A dense white cloud plume produced as a stream of lava flowed into the sea at Surtsey, Iceland, on July 24, 1964. The source of the lava is the lava fountain silhouetted against the sky at the right center of the picture. The highest point of Surtsey, at center, is about 570 feet above sea level. This picture is a composite made from two pictures taken a short time apart. (Photo by Sveinbjörn Björnsson)

FIG. 35. The Woodcock and Spencer experiment simulated the action of the sea on volcanic outpourings. They sprayed molten lava with sea water and trapped the steam cloud in a cardboard cylinder. Microscopic examination subsequently revealed the presence of sea-salt particles in the cylinder.

of thousands of times greater than is produced by bubbles in the sea.

In view of this they suggested that it just might be possible that the splashing of sea water on only a few square kilometers of hot lava could produce as many sea-salt particles per second as are normally produced by all the oceans of the earth. They went on to point out that if the giant salt particles were really aiding in the formation of raindrops (Chapter 3), then, at times when a number of volcanoes were erupting and hot

lava was coming into contact with the sea, large-scale
changes in the weather might occur.

This was not the first time the suggestion had been
made that erupting volcanoes might influence the
weather, but it was the first time that attention was
focused on sea-salt particles that were produced by the
interaction of volcanoes and the sea.

It is not yet known whether volcano-produced sea-
salt particles can or cannot cause a significant change
in the weather, local or otherwise. But there is little
doubt that under the right conditions the splashing of
sea water on hot lava is nature's most effective way by
far, area for area, for the production of sea-salt particles.

A 120-Year-Old Signpost

During the weeks that Woodcock and Spencer were
firing up their do-it-yourself volcano, I often would
watch the "pouring of the lava into the sea" and the
formation of the cloud. Although I saw this experiment performed many times, it never occurred to me
that there might be something extraordinary about it,
other than its fantastic ability to manufacture sea-salt
particles.

But one day, perhaps a year later, I was in the li-
brary pursuing what you might call a hobby of mine,
reading the writings of the scientific adventurers who
worked in the last century and before. I had just pulled
off the shelf a rather dusty volume, the British *Philosophical Magazine* for the year 1841, and was idly
thumbing through the pages. On page 100 I stopped,
for there was a paper on the electricity of steam by a
French physicist named Athanase Peltier.

It appears that the workers in certain mills in England at that time were afraid to approach the steam

engines. And for good reason. When the steam engines were in operation they became highly electrified and gave off sparks to the air, or else gave a shock to anyone who dared to touch them.

Peltier was one of several persons who were interested in finding the explanation of this curious sparking. He had an idea and it went like this. The water in the boilers of the steam engine must have some salt and impurities in it, and perhaps the splashing of this salty water against the hot walls of the boiler makes an electrically charged cloud. The charged cloud leaves the boiler through the stack, and the equal and opposite charge stays behind on the boiler to shock the workmen.

To demonstrate his idea, Peltier connected an electrometer (an instrument to detect extremely small amounts of electricity) to a hot platinum dish (his boiler), and splashed a drop of diluted sea water (the water in the boiler) on it. The needle of the electrometer wiggled; the drop on the hot surface was generating electricity that was being carried away from the surface.

I do not know if Peltier was on the right track in trying to explain boiler electricity, but the minute I read about his drop of diluted sea water on a hot surface I thought of—you guessed it—Woodcock and Spencer's drop of sea water on hot lava. If Peltier found that a charge was carried away to the air, then why wouldn't the cloud that Woodcock and Spencer produced also carry electricity? And why wouldn't any cloud that is produced when lava flows into the sea be charged?

Here, from 120 years in the past, was a signpost (Fig. 36) which pointed the way to an experiment that might show a connection between volcanoes, the sea, and electricity. The direction in which it pointed was

Fig. 36. Peltier's paper of 1841, like all good guideposts, pointed in two directions.

unmistakably clear to anyone who knew about the work of Woodcock and Spencer. It required nothing more than a dim awareness that a new research trail was crossing one that had been blazed over a hundred years ago.

A good signpost tells you not only what to expect in the trail ahead but also what you will find in the trail behind. Peltier in his paper referred to the papers of others who were interested in similar problems. I found these papers, read them, and discovered that they, too, were signposts that in turn pointed backward down the trail to still earlier signposts. One led to another, and eventually the beginning of the trail was found. It was in a paper by the great Italian scientist,

Alessandro Volta, in the *Philosophical Transactions of the Royal Society of London* for the year 1782.

Volta had yet to usher in the electrical age with his invention of the world's first battery.* In 1782 he was interested in (among other things) the idea that electricity could be generated by the simple evaporation of water. He tried again and again to show this by connecting pans of water to his electrometer. He fully expected that the evaporating water vapor would carry electricity away from the pan, leaving it charged with the opposite sign. But he never found this to occur.

One day, however, he happened to be in London and was demonstrating some of his wonderful electrical experiments to the scientists of the Royal Society. When he came to his evaporation experiment, he apparently got the idea suddenly that maybe his experiment had not worked because the water had not evaporated fast enough. And what better way, thought Volta, to evaporate water rapidly, than to drop it onto something hot? He took a metal dish full of hot coals, connected it to his electrometer, and threw some water into it.

What do you think happened? The water must have sizzled and foamed, and produced a cloud, but, most important of all, and to Volta's great delight, the electrometer indicated that negative electricity had been produced in the dish. Thus the cloud must have been charged with positive electricity. Volta concluded immediately that the experiment proved that the evaporation of water generated electricity, and he went on to speculate that this might be the answer to the mystery of the positive charge of the atmosphere (Chapter 7). After all, the surface of the earth is about 70 per cent

* That came in 1800. The significance of that invention was recognized by naming the unit of electrical potential, the *volt*, in his honor.

water, and there is plenty of evaporation of water into the air.

What do you think? Volta had proved that an electrically charged cloud could be produced by throwing water on hot coals. There was no doubt about that. But did evaporation produce the electricity? Is not Volta's experiment, like Peltier's, suggestive of the one done by Woodcock and Spencer? When they splashed sea water on hot lava they found that during the evaporation sea-salt particles were produced. Though Volta's water may not have been very salty, maybe tiny droplets of water were thrown outward from the hot coals. And isn't it just possible that the electricity was carried by these microscopic droplets and not by the water vapor?

From Volta's paper I made my way back up the research trail and found that this question had been debated for the next one hundred years. Some scientists said, "Of course evaporation can generate electricity," and they "proved" it by repeating Volta's experiment. Others, aware that the road to true understanding is not easily followed, made their way more slowly. One such man was Michael Faraday of England, the master experimentalist of his day. Faraday, in a brilliant series of experiments, showed that the electricity produced by steam clouds did *not* come from the evaporation of water, but from some unknown frictional effects associated with the tiny droplets in the cloud.

For forty years after Faraday's work the experiments continued. And then the trail ended. In 1882, exactly one hundred years after Volta had first opened the subject, it came to a close in a paper in the *Philosophical Transactions* by an English scientist by the name of Freeman. Interestingly enough, Freeman produced charged clouds by dropping salty water on hot metal. After the publication of Freeman's paper, interest in the generation of electricity by liquids on hot surfaces disappeared. The mists of time descended on the trail, and by the turn of the century it was completely forgotten.

Hot Lava, Sea Water, and Electricity

But let us return to the present. I have taken you on this detour into the past to show you that the work of those who have come before, even though forgotten, often contains the key to the scientific problems of the present. And, as mentioned earlier, though it may not produce the perfect key, it can point the way, clearly and unmistakably, to new ideas and new experiments to be performed. Thus it was with the Woodcock and Spencer experiment. It seemed almost certain that their clouds over the hot lava should carry electricity, as did the clouds produced by Volta and others of his time. To find out, all we had to do was to try the experiment.

And we did. Our experiment was basically the same as that shown in Fig. 35. The only addition was a thin wire connecting an electrometer to the lava, and a wire mesh cage that surrounded the lava and protected it from the influence of stray electrical charges in the room.* It was similar to Volta's experiment, except that molten lava was substituted for the hot coals. The surface of the lava was heated until it melted and gave off a red-orange glow. Sea water was dashed on it, and a cloud rose into the air. At the same time the needle of the electrometer began to move in the direction which indicated that negative electricity was coming from the hot lava. The positive electricity was in the cloud!

* Remember, in Chapter 7 we discussed how jet drops could become charged by electrostatic induction. A similar thing could happen with a waterdrop on a hot surface.

The experiment was repeated many times, and each time the cloud carried positive electricity. The cloud produced by a single drop of sea water carried about 1,000,000,000 elementary charges.

On the basis of these experiments it seemed probable that the volcanic cloud through which Woodcock flew had been highly charged with positive electricity. And if that was so, then it is quite likely that all clouds that are created when sea water strikes molten lava will be positively charged, maybe even to the point of producing lightning.

An experiment that demonstrates the production of electricity when sea water strikes a hot surface can be performed very easily, and without the aid of an electrometer (which is quite expensive). As this experiment is extremely interesting and fun to do, I'm going to show you how it is done. You'll be able to prove for yourself the things we've been talking about. And it wouldn't surprise me at all if a few of you discovered some facts that now are known only by nature.

Before we go directly to the heart of the experiment, I would like to tell you about the curious behavior of a waterdrop on a very hot surface. It's called the Leidenfrost Phenomenon, named after Johann Leidenfrost, a German medical doctor who, in 1756, was the first to make a detailed study of these strange drops. If you're not aware of this behavior, you will, when you first see it, become convinced that the world of common sense has been turned upside down. An understanding of this paradox is necessary before you attempt the charge experiment.

If you heat a frying pan for a minute or so until it is hot (300 to 400°F or about 150 to 200°C), but not too hot, and then place a drop of water in it, you'll find that the drop will bubble and boil and within a second have completely evaporated. A small steam cloud rising above the pan is all that remains. All right, you say, there's nothing curious about that. But now heat the pan for five minutes or more until it is very hot (in excess of 700°F or 370°C); then place the waterdrop on it. What do you suppose happens? Common sense would say that if a hot frying pan can evaporate the drop in about a second, then, obviously, a very hot frying pan can do it in less time. But in this case, common sense would strike out. You are faced with the Leidenfrost Phenomenon. A drop in a very hot frying pan remains unperturbed about its predicament, and, like a graceful ice skater, glides slowly and smoothly in long swooping arcs from one side of the pan to the other (Fig. 37). Sometimes it stops for a minute or so and vibrates or distorts itself to break in two like a giant amoeba. But regardless of what it does, many minutes will pass before evaporation causes it to disappear.

The explanation of the behavior of these curious drops that appear to float across the surface of the pan is just that—they do float. They float on a thin layer of water vapor that holds them a small fraction of a millimeter above the surface. This cushion of water vapor, thin as it is, is a good insulator against the heat of the very hot surface just below. As the water vapor cushion apparently cannot form unless the surface is very hot, a drop on a cooler surface makes contact with the metal and quickly evaporates.

The most interesting behavior of all is found at intermediate temperatures, where it appears that the drop can't decide whether to behave as if on a hot or a very hot surface. So it compromises and rapidly alternates between making contact with the surface and bouncing into the air above (Fig. 37). Like a miniature jackhammer it strikes the surface some 20 to 30 times per second. On each bounce it sprays into the air a multitude of tiny droplets. All this is accompanied by the well-known sizzling sound.

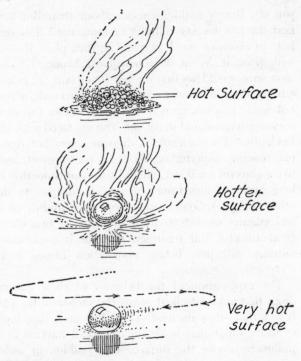

Hot Surface

Hotter surface

Very hot surface

FIG. 37. Drop of water in hot frying pan exhibits unexpected behavior. At 300 to 400°F (at top) it foams and evaporates in a second but at higher temperature (center) it bounces and sizzles, takes many seconds to disappear. On surface over 700°F (bottom) drop glides about on cushion of vapor, may not evaporate for minutes.

We can classify the behavior of a drop in these three temperature regimes—the hot, intermediate, and very hot—by referring to it as the evaporating drop, the bouncing drop*, and the floating drop. Would you

* On hot lava a drop shows very little of the pure bouncing mode. Its behavior is a sort of a combination between bouncing and evaporating. This difference probably reflects the fact that the rate at which heat can flow through lava (the thermal conductivity) is much less than for metal. Therefore, even though

care to guess which of these generates the most electricity? Let's find out by doing that experiment I mentioned a while back.

Frying Pan Electricity

This experiment can be done with a metal frying pan*, some aluminum foil (bought in a grocery store), and one of those 300 volt batteries we used in the last chapter in connection with the Millikan chamber experiment. Place the frying pan on a tripod or frame of some sort (anything that can withstand the heat from a hot frying pan) so the handle will be about 35 cm above the table. The frame should stand on a non-conductor of electricity. A dry wood or plastic surface may work, but I'd suggest that you set the frame on a polyethylene bag (also found in a grocery store).

Next take a pair of scissors or a razor blade, and cut off a long narrow strip of aluminum foil (0.2 cm wide or less and about 30 cm long) and tie it to the end of the handle (Fig. 38). Electricity must be able to flow freely from the frying pan to the strip; to be doubly sure that you have a good electrical connection, take a piece of aluminum foil and crinkle it up tightly around the end of the handle and the strip.

You may be puzzled why we have that thin strip of aluminum hanging from the handle. If any electricity is generated in the frying pan it will spread out all over

---

the lava may be extremely hot, the drop can cool the surface locally. The vapor film cannot be maintained because heat cannot flow fast enough to the cool area.

* Don't use one coated with Teflon or fitted with a plastic handle. These materials don't conduct electricity. Of course, you could use a piece of lava, but I don't recommend it. You'll need an oxy-acetylene torch, and it should be used only by those who have had experience with it. Stay with the metal; you'll be able to generate a charge just as easily—in fact, even better than with lava.

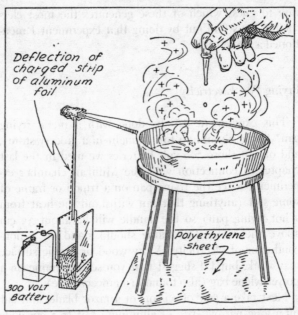

Deflection of
charged strip
of aluminum
foil

Polyethylene
sheet

300 VOLT
Battery

FIG. 38. Electricity generated by drops of sea water on a
hot frying pan can be detected with this simple apparatus.
Clouds carry away positive charge. Negative charge remains
on pan and aluminum foil, which is deflected toward
positively charged plate. See text for complications that
can enter into this experiment.

the pan and some will go down the strip. The strip
becomes charged.

Can you think of an easy way in which we could detect that charge and what sign it is? There is at least
one way to do it very nicely; we can build a simple
device that can be used to make the charged strip
swing to one side or the other.*

Take a couple of pieces of cardboard (about 10 cm
square) and wrap them individually with aluminum

* Now you can see why I suggested using a thin strip of aluminum foil. It is extremely light and will swing fairly easily.

foil. Tape one end of each of the foil plates onto the opposite sides of a block of wood that is about 2 cm thick (Fig. 38). Now connect the positive side of your battery to one plate, and the negative side to the other, and ground one of the plates. For safety reasons mentioned in connection with the Millikan chamber experiment (Fig. 32), include a carbon resistor (of about a million ohms resistance) in this circuit. That's all there is to it; you're just about ready to perform the experiment.

Position the plates so that the aluminum strip hangs only about 0.2 or 0.3 cm (and no more) down between them. If the strip is too long, use scissors to shorten it. It must not be blown around by breezes. You may have to keep doors and windows closed.

The time has come to heat the frying pan, with a Bunsen burner or perhaps a hot plate. You could heat it on a stove and then quickly place it on the frame. When the pan is hot, flick a few drops of sea water into it and watch the end of the aluminum strip. If the drops either evaporate quickly or float you won't detect any motion of the strip. No significant generation of electricity has occurred. But if the drops bounce and sizzle, you'll see the strip move toward the positive plate.* Several bouncing drops will usually generate enough electricity to charge the strip to the point where it's attracted all the way to the positive plate. It will strike the plate, exchange charge with it, and spring back to approximately center position. Can you deduce from this attraction the sign of the charge on the cloud produced by the bouncing drops? Since the strip was attracted to the positive plate, it must have carried a negative charge. This charge, given to

* Only if the frying pan is clean and free from all grease and cooking oils. It may require several minutes of heating to burn off the organic material. Also, tap water and other types of water may give a different response. Try it.

the frying pan by some action of the bouncing drops, must have been accompanied by a positive charge which was carried into the air by the cloud.

Although this experiment is easy to do, it is just as easy to be misled by it. There are a number of other ways in which the strip might be made to move, and these effects could be confused with the charging effect we are looking for. Be on your guard.*

No one yet knows why a drop of sea water on a hot metal or lava surface produces a charged cloud; but it appears to be generated along with the sea-salt particles and tiny droplets that are created by the bouncing

---

* To begin with there are two potential sources of extraneous charging that plague all electrostatic experiments of this type. You should be on the lookout for them. The first is that some of the charge that you measure might be on the drop before it strikes the pan, and has nothing whatever to do with the bouncing drop. It's very easy to show whether this is true or not; think about it. If it is true you can eliminate it. The second source of extraneous charge is the one we met in Chapter 7 in connection with the jet drops—electrostatic induction. I'll let you devise a method to check for that also, and to eliminate it if it exists. The techniques used in Chapter 7 are equally applicable here.

There is still another induction effect you should be aware of. You can demonstrate it easily. Ground both plates and the pan. Now unground the plates and connect the 300 volt battery (with one side grounded) across them. Did you see the strip suddenly move about 0.1 cm toward the ungrounded plate? This slight attraction will not interfere with the experiment, providing you keep the plates separated by about 2 cm.

A final induction effect that could lead to confusion is one that involves electrical images (you will find image attractions discussed in a good physics book). What it means here is that the charged strip will be attracted toward the nearest plate, *even though both plates are grounded*. But, again, if you keep the strip about a centimeter from the plates, this effect should not bother you.

You can see this effect if you move the grounded plates so that the strip is only about 0.2 cm from one of the plates. Now drop a few drops of sea water in the hot frying pan and you'll see the strip move and strike the plate. In this way you don't even need a battery to detect the charge on the strip, but, of course, you can't tell whether it's positive or negative.

drops. The evaporation of water alone cannot account for it.

The time has come to leave this chapter. We have traveled far from the eruption of Kilauea, where molten lava poured into the sea to produce steam clouds that rose rapidly into the air. Let's quickly retrace our path.

A chance remark by an eyewitness to this event prompted Woodcock to wonder whether the steam clouds might contain more than just "steam." By laboratory experiments and by an airplane flight through these clouds, Woodcock and Spencer found that they did contain sea-salt particles. From that point we jumped back to the last century and saw how the accidental discovery of an old, forgotten research trail provided the clue that these clouds might be charged with electricity. With that clue we carried out laboratory experiments which showed that the clouds carried a positive charge.

In our final chapter we shall leave the laboratory far behind us and head out into the North Atlantic to visit a volcano that erupted through the surface of the sea. There we will witness the eruption and find that the clouds are electrified. But, more important, we will look closely to see whether any of this electricity could have been generated by the contact of molten lava with sea water.

Chapter 10

A VOLCANO
AT THE SURFACE OF THE SEA

After some hours we came in sight of a solitary rock
in the ocean, forming a mighty vault, through which
the foaming waves poured with intense fury. The
islets of Westman appeared to leap from the ocean,
being so low in the water as scarcely to be seen until
you were right upon them. From that moment the
schooner was steered to the westward in order to
round Cape Reykjaness, the western point of Iceland.*

Jules Verne's Professor Von Hardwigg and the professor's nephew Harry were clearing the tiny Westman†
Islands, just off the southern shore of Iceland. The
great adventure lay ahead of them. Their destination
was the glacier-capped volcano of Snaefells, perched on
the end of a long peninsula on the western side of
Iceland, 150 miles northwest of the Westman Islands.
The crater of Snaefells was to be their gateway to the
center of the earth.

It is unlikely that even the imagination of Jules
Verne could have foreseen that some day the Westman
Islands would be witness to a real-world spectacle to
rival any of the fictional ones which flowed from his
pen. When he wrote, "The islets of Westman appeared

* From the novel by Jules Verne, A *Journey to the Centre of
the Earth*. Cape Reykjanes is now spelled with a single "s" at the
end.

† The proper spelling is Vestmannaeyjar, but you'll also see it
spelled Vestmann or Westman.

to leap from the ocean . . ." he was only using a delightful metaphor to indicate the smallness of the islands. But the passage of years has turned that metaphor into a fact. An islet of Westman has indeed leaped from the ocean. In November of 1963, without preliminary rumblings, a volcano suddenly burst through the surface of the sea. A new islet of Westman had been born.

The Birth of Surtsey

It was early in the morning. The fishermen had just finished laying their lines a few miles west of the southernmost of the Westman Islands. These men of the fishing boat *Isleifur II* had done this many times before, and there was nothing different on this morning of November 14, 1963 to suggest that it would be anything but another normal, uneventful day of fishing.

The lines in place, the crew went below for a well-earned cup of coffee. At five minutes before seven, Árni Gudmundsson, the engineer, wandered out on deck. That's curious, what's that smell? He peered around, found nothing unusual, and went back below. At about the same time the captain, Gudmar Tomasson, came topside and he, too, had the same experience. It was a strange smell but nothing to get alarmed about. He went below to his bunk.

At seven-thirty he was suddenly awakened by the cook, Olafur Vestmann. Olafur had been on watch, and a few minutes before had had the peculiar feeling that the boat was moving as if caught in a whirlpool. In the distance, through the early morning haze, he could make out a dark object. A rock? It can't be a rock; there are no rocks around here. He looked again, and realized it was smoke. It was then that he hurried below to wake the captain. Maybe a ship was on fire.

The captain called the Westman Islands radio station. Had they received any S.O.S. calls? They had not. If it's not a rock or a burning ship, what is it? He trained his binoculars on the smoke, and soon was able to make out dark columns of ash and cloud that were rising up through the surface of the sea. For the first time he realized that they were watching a volcano erupt from the sea.

They moved toward it for a better look, but increasing turbulence in the sea prevented them from approaching any closer than about a half mile. This was close enough; the eruption was increasing in intensity. Huge columns of ash, stones, and cloud were being hurled upward from the sea. A plume of cloud continued to rise high in the sky like smoke from a giant fire in the sea. By mid-morning the plume had reached a height of about 12,000 feet, and by late afternoon about 20,000 feet, almost four miles above the sea. It became visible to the inhabitants of Reykjavik, the capital city of Iceland, seventy miles to the northwest. High in the atmosphere and caught in the rays of the setting sun, it was vividly and beautifully etched against the evening sky.

As darkness descended on that first day, the explosions went on, and rocks and ash-streaked clouds continued to be thrust violently into the atmosphere. And yet there was no island or volcanic crater to be seen at the surface of the sea. The events of that day were only birth pangs; sometime in the night the volcanic island of Surtsey* was born.

In the cold light of morning the new island was seen for the first time. For many days, it had been building itself up unseen from the floor of the ocean, more than 400 feet below, and now it had finally burst through the surface of the sea to thrust itself thirty feet into

* This name was derived from *Surtur*, a giant who appears in Norse mythology.

the air. The sea was pouring into a large fissure and presumably was striking the molten lava. Explosions shook the new volcano, and fountains of ash and cloud rocketed skyward. The island grew rapidly under a rain of ash; four days later it was about 200 feet high and 2000 feet in length.

The Westman Islanders could lay claim to a new addition to their island group. Surtsey lay about twelve miles southwest of their main island of Heimaey, but only about three miles west-southwest of the pinpoint-sized island of Geirfuglasker (Fig. 39). In addition to being the newest piece of land in Iceland, Surtsey had the honor of being the southernmost. Iceland now extended south to a latitude of 63°18'.

Surtsey continued to grow. Within two weeks after birth the island was larger, with the exception of Heimaey, than any of the other Westman Islands. The eruptions showed no sign of stopping, and by that time the story of the birth of this amazing volcanic island had spread around the world.*

A Trip to Iceland

Icelandic scientists began their studies of Surtsey on the very day that it came into being. By eleven o'clock of that day several of them were flying overhead to make the first of a long series of detailed observations on the nature of the eruptions, and on the growth of Surtsey.

One of the first United States scientists to visit Surtsey was Paul Bauer, of American University. On the twenty-eighth of November 1963 he saw Surtsey in full eruption. When he returned from his trip he reported

---

* My account of the birth of Surtsey is based on the book, *Surtsey*, by Sigurdur Thorarinsson. Published in 1964, it may be obtained from Almenna Bókafélagid, Reykjavik, Iceland.

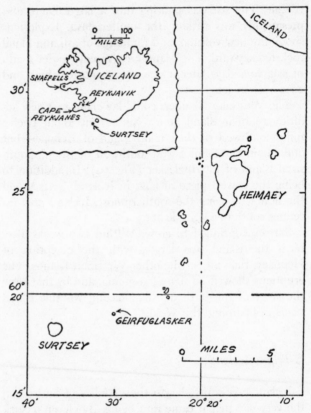

FIG. 39. Volcanic island of Surtsey lies off southern coast of Iceland.

on what he and the Icelandic scientists had seen. They had seen, in addition to the explosions and the violent ejection of ash and cloud, something else; the ejection plumes were occasionally ablaze with numerous short, zig-zag flashes of lightning. The products of the eruption clearly were charged with electricity. But where the charge came from and what sign it was, no one knew.

At the Office of Naval Research in Washington, James Hughes, who had heard about the volcanic lightning (Plate XII), got in touch with a number of American scientists who might be interested in studying Surtsey's lightning. Through such studies we might get some clues as to how charge is generated in volcanic eruptions and how much of a role is played by sea water. And, who knows, maybe we could extrapolate something of what we learn about charge generation in volcanic eruptions to charge generation in thunderstorms. Through Hughes' initiative, a trip to Surtsey was planned. And so it was that on the tenth of February 1964, several of us found ourselves leaving Washington, D.C., aboard the United States Naval Research Laboratory's Constellation airplane: destination Iceland.

That night, not yet even halfway to Iceland, we landed at the American base in Argentia, Newfoundland. The next morning dawned bleak and cold, and with it we were off for the final 1800-mile journey out over the North Atlantic. We passed Cape Farewell on the southern tip of Greenland, flew up Greenland's eastern coast, and across Denmark Strait toward Iceland. As we flew across Denmark Strait, the air temperature rose. This change was expected, for we were flying out to sea; the frigid west winds sweeping out of Canada and Greenland were being warmed in their passage over the relatively warm waters of the North Atlantic.

By mid-afternoon the shores of Iceland loomed through the hazy air. We still had an hour or two of daylight left. Why not fly down and take a look at Surtsey? We banked to the right, flew off to the southeast, and, like Professor Von Hardwigg, cleared Cape Reykjanes. But there was one small difference; he knew exactly where his volcano was; we didn't. No one on the plane—pilots, crew, or scientists—had any idea where Surtsey was, other than that it was somewhere off the Westman Islands.

No matter; all we had to do was to find a huge cloud column in the sky; the volcano would be at the bottom of the column. We quickly spotted it far off on the horizon and headed toward it. As we came closer, it was clear that the top of the column was at a height of about 18,000 feet; the other end, seen from the airplane far above, was anchored at the surface of the sea in a black circular spot fringed with a ring of foam. This was Surtsey.

The plane dropped down to an altitude of a few hundred feet, and the black spot of Surtsey turned into a mountainous pile of ash about 560 feet high. The ring of foam was from waves breaking and running up on gently sloping black sand beaches that ran nearly three miles around the island. A large, gaping conical depression at one end of the island was the vent which gave birth to Surtsey. It had been active until just a few days before, when a second vent farther to the northwest had opened up.

Only the top and outer edge of this new vent could be seen; the mouth was completely hidden behind large fountains of ash, rocks, and dense clouds that were streaking continuously upward from the crater. This monstrous fire hose, spraying the incredible mixture a thousand feet or more into the air, was also arching hot rocks out over the sea. We could not see these rocks, but as they crashed into the ocean they produced brilliant white discs, some perhaps fifty feet across. A dozen or more of these pads of foam dotted a calm sea offshore.

We flew past the volcano several more times, and through the top of the eruption cloud. Then we left Surtsey, headed for the mainland of Iceland, and landed at the airport in Keflavik. Our first view of

Surtsey was a brief one, but we had not seen the last of that volcano.

The plan of action for the following week was simple and direct; the scientists from the Naval Research Laboratory would make daily flights to Surtsey and learn what they could about the electrical nature of the eruption cloud by flying beside it, under it, above it, and even through it. But three of us decided to leave the plane and make our way as best we could to the Westman Islands. There we hoped to charter a fishing boat, put instruments on it, and get as close as possible to the volcano.

About midnight the next evening, James Hughes, Charles Moore, of Arthur D. Little, Inc., and I found ourselves aboard a small coastal steamer slowly feeling its way through the darkness of Reykjavik harbor, to begin an all-night journey to the island of Heimaey in the Westman Islands. As we rounded Cape Reykjanes, the short, disturbed motion of the water gave way to the long, undulating swell of the North Atlantic. With that, sleep came easily.

When we awoke, the rhythmic throbbing of the engines had stilled; we were in the harbor at Heimaey. We stepped out in the bright morning sun and found ourselves amid a tight cluster of fishing boats. One of the richest fishing grounds in the whole Atlantic Ocean is around the Westman Islands, and this harbor is the center of activity. The inhabitants of the town, which hugs one side of the harbor, live in dwellings whose red, white, or green roofs provide a splash of color in marked contrast to the somber, dark hues of the volcanic soil and broken bits of lava covering the island. On the other side of the harbor, thrust up violently from the sea by some past volcanic fury, giant ridges and gnarled fingers of rock tower several hundred feet over the town. These volcanic rocks give mute testimony that the birth of Heimaey, as reckoned by the geological clock, had occurred only a few seconds before the appearance of Surtsey. That morning thousands of white sea birds dotted these dark cliffs like a light sprinkle of snow.

Before the day was over, we had secured lodgings in this small fishing village and had made arrangements with the captain of the fishing boat *Haraldur** to make the trip to Surtsey. Moore, amid shouts of encouragement from Hughes and me, shinnied up the mast of the *Haraldur* (Fig. 40) and at the top attached a sharp, pointed rod. Through this rod, a descendant of Benjamin Franklin's lightning rod, we hoped to measure the flow of electricity between the boat and the air that we were certain would occur when we approached Surtsey's volcanic cloud. If it didn't occur, then the cloud could not be very highly charged.

A long wire antenna was stretched horizontally seven or eight feet above the deck†; this was to be used to measure the vertical potential gradient of the atmosphere (Chapter 7). Highly insulated wires connected the sharp point and the antenna to instruments and pen recorders within the cabin. We were ready to begin the final leg of the trip to Surtsey.

But the elements were not about to let us go. For over two days the howling winter winds of the North Atlantic turned the water outside the haven of the harbor into a jumbled mixture of foam-capped peaks rising up from undulating blue-green valleys. We, in our eagerness to get to Surtsey, would foolishly have risked the trip, but the captain of the *Haraldur* took one look at the sea, shook his head, and said maybe tomorrow.

The days were put to good use. Vonnegut had left

---

* This was the same boat that Moore's colleague, Bernard Vonnegut (Chapter 7) had used to visit Surtsey the week before.

† A small amount of the radioactive element polonium was attached to the wire. The presence of the radioactivity enables the wire to respond rapidly to changes in the potential of the atmosphere.

Fig. 40. Pointed metal rod attached to mast measured flow of electricity between fishing boat *Haraldur* and the air around Surtsey.

some special cameras which he and Moore had used in lightning studies. One of these was trained on Surtsey, twelve miles to the southwest, and kept running night and day. If there was any lightning in the volcanic cloud, especially at night, the camera would photograph it.

By day, from the high, steep volcanic ridges on Heimaey, we could see Surtsey. It looked like a coal-black saucer floating upside down on the horizon, with smoke issuing from one side. As dusk fell we could see short quick flashes of light which could be nothing else but lightning. In proof of this, Moore's portable transistor radio clicked with static each time we saw the flashes from Surtsey. It was beyond any doubt; Surtsey was generating enough electricity to produce lightning. But how much electricity? And what sign?

Sunday, the sixteenth of February, dawned bright and clear. The day was delightfully warm and the winds were light. The rough sea of the day before had disappeared; in its place was a calmer swell that the *Haraldur* and its captain would tolerate. In short, it was the kind of Sunday that anyone would choose to visit a volcano.

About noontime, with a few townspeople looking on, we pulled away from the dock and, steaming slowly out of the harbor and past the high volcanic cliffs, turned southwest toward Surtsey.

The Visit to Surtsey

The *Haraldur* rocked slowly as she moved through the ocean swell, and small waves smacked against her sides. At times the bow dipped deep, and necklaces of water sparkled in the air before breaking on the foredeck. Overhead, the sea birds swooped and soared in long, graceful spirals. On the distant horizon we could see that Surtsey was ejecting vertical pillars of ash and cloud. We were in luck; the wind was out of the southeast; it would be possible to get close to the active vent on the southwest side of Surtsey and not have the eruption cloud blown over us.

The potential gradient was positive, holding steady, and appeared to be what one might normally find near the surface of the sea in clear weather. We had been out for about half an hour and Surtsey still loomed on the horizon, but now the island began to grow slowly and take shape. The dark shadows took on detail. High up on the slopes of ash the surface was smooth but pockmarked with craters made by falling rocks. Around the perimeter of Surtsey, where storm waves had earlier taken huge bites from the island, the smooth slopes gave way to short steep cliffs.

Every few seconds dark clouds rose from the vent on the other side of the island. The wind spread them out to form a huge dark vertical wall, which ran from the island to as far as we could see on our right, and from the sea upward to nearly the zenith. On the left we saw clear air, sea birds, and sunlight; on the right, a curtain of ash and the near darkness of night. Here and there vertical pillars of cloud broke the curtain; from far above, long fingers of ash (and maybe water) streamed downward to the sea.

By now we had expected to hear the roar of the volcano, but an eerie silence prevailed. Surtsey seemed to be performing in pantomime. Then every so often a sudden sharp crack, like a rifle shot, shattered the silence. We were mystified, and for a while thought the sound might be caused by rocks falling on the island. We looked more closely but could see no large rocks crashing into the island.

The *Haraldur* was now closer to the curtain of darkness, and every minute or so a flash of lightning darted out from the lower part of the clouds. A few seconds later the mysterious crack was heard, but now it was no longer mysterious. It was clear that it was thunder. None of us had ever heard thunder like this before; we were familiar with the type that booms and reverberates for many seconds, like the sound of a hundred cannon all going off at slightly different times. Surtsey's thunder did not sound like this, probably because the lightning strokes were only a thousand feet or so in length. Thus the sound from every point in the lightning channel arrived at the *Haraldur* at about the same time, producing the sharp crack. A thunderstorm lightning stroke, on the other hand, may be 10,000 feet or more in length, and the time interval between the arrival of the first sound waves and those from the far end of the lightning channel may be several seconds.* This difference in path length of the sound waves produces the long drawn-out booming that we usually associate with thunder.

We were still to the east of the island but now turned left to pass by the southern side of Surtsey and approach the very throat of the volcano. Soon we could see it, and, as if to welcome us, Surtsey put on a grand display of the forces at its command. The sea had found its way through a large gaping V-shaped opening that was clearly visible in the seaward side of the crater. Tons of sea water presumably came into contact with the molten lava that was surging upward through the throat of the crater. There were violent explosions and upheavals that belched ash, cloud, rocks, and sea water in one vast mixture (Plate XIII). Sometimes the eruption continued for a minute or more, while an immense fountain was spraying a black, ash-covered jet 1000 feet into the air. The jet would change from black to a black-and-white striped appearance, and, near the top where great cauliflower masses of cloud were forming from the condensing steam, the jet became almost completely white. At times the eruptions would cease, as if Surtsey were resting from its strenuous exercises. The bottom of the crater filled completely with sea water, and sea birds swooped low over the now quiet surface. Only a gentle steaming disturbed the surface, and we approached to within 300 feet of the crater. But no closer, for the giant was only slumbering.

Surtsey would awaken suddenly, the water in the center of the crater beginning to bubble, and within a

* The speed of sound in air is about 1100 feet per second.

second or two, ash and cloud would be hurled upward and outward at speeds of up to 200 miles per hour. Like a huge black and white balloon being inflated, the outpouring swelled quickly until its top had reached a height of over 2000 feet. From the surface of these clouds secondary explosions hurled huge feathered spears of cloud and ash that fanned outward and finally arched earthward in long exquisite streamers silhouetted against the clear blue sky. Surely man, for all his genius, could never compete with nature in composing such splendor and beauty in violent upheaval.

Lightning and Surtsey-type thunder occurred during all these eruptions, but most exciting to us were the traces drawn on the chart by the pens automatically recording the potential gradient and the flow of electricity through the sharp point atop the mast (Fig. 40). At the start of an eruption the potential gradient was not much more than +100 volts per meter, a normal value to find at sea. But as the clouds billowed upward (Plate XIV), the gradient rose rapidly to several thousand volts per meter. And then, simultaneous with a lightning stroke, the gradient would fall back to nearly 100 volts per meter. This reversal occurred repeatedly, and the pen traced a sawtooth curve. A similar curve was traced by the pen recording the current flow between the air and the sharp point. The stronger the positive potential gradient, the stronger was the positive current that flowed from the air to the point.*

It looked as if a positive charge was being carried up from the crater by the eruption clouds. The increase in potential gradient and the point discharge current

* This type of current is known by several names—point discharge current, corona current, or St. Elmo's fire. The last is especially well known to sailors as the flame-like glow that is sometimes seen from exposed points on a ship's rigging during a thunderstorm or stormy weather.

reflected the buildup of the charge. Finally, like a water-filled paper bag about to burst, the surrounding air could stand no more increase in potential gradient and broke down. A lightning stroke occurred, and the charge poured down through the lightning channel to the ground.

At about half-past one the eruption ceased and all was quiet. This was the intermission before the grand finale. At three o'clock Surtsey came to life again with eruptions that were far more intense and continuous than any heretofore. Great fountains played continuously and the immense curtain of ash and cloud columns loomed above us again. Looking up at it from the *Haraldur* bobbing offshore, we felt as if we were at the base of a thousand-foot-high Niagara Falls. Torrents of ash were cascading downward, and rocks plunging into the sea sent up white geysers of water. Although we were upwind of this spectacle some ash did reach us, but it was very fine and barely noticeable.

Amid frequent flashes of lightning and cracks of thunder, the pen moved rapidly back and forth recording the now familiar sawtooth changes in the potential gradient. I remember running into the cabin to observe these sudden changes while the eruption was at its height. The pen snapped back with every lightning flash that I could see, and sometimes when I saw no flash. When this happened I began to count off the seconds—1001, 1002—and then, crack! the thunder reached us. The lightning flash must have occurred hidden from view deep in that dark curtain.

At the height of the eruption there were so many exciting and wondrous things going on that we were like children at a great circus trying to watch the action in all three rings at the same time. Colossal jets streaking upward into the blue and the vast waterfall of ash tumbling down to the island and the sea shared the center ring. High above the far ring the aerialists held forth, beautiful mushroom clouds turning themselves inside out as they sprang upward. Here and there spinning smoke rings of cloud could be seen (Plate XV), and descending from some of the clouds, like long, sinewy, twisting ropes, were whirlwinds. In the near ring the thunder and lightning dominated the scene, while clouds rushed down the sides of the crater and rolled out over the sea. There was too much going on at once for our senses to absorb, and we hoped that our movie cameras were capturing on film this magnificent spectacle.

The afternoon shadows were lengthening and it was time for us to return to Heimaey. Surtsey was still in vigorous eruption as we steamed away. The potential gradient decreased slowly until, when Surtsey's cloud was low on the horizon and glowing red in the setting sun, it reached and maintained the low value it had had at the start of the trip.

We wondered just what this potential gradient record would finally tell us, whether it would agree with the findings of those who had flown around Surtsey all week, and with what Bernard Vonnegut had found in his visit to Surtsey the week before. We were to wait more than a month before learning that all the measurements appeared to point to one conclusion: the clouds rising from Surtsey's crater were highly charged with positive electricity. The flow of this charge from the crater constituted a positive current of about 0.03 ampere. Though only about 3 per cent of the current generated in a thunderstorm, the 0.03 ampere was sufficient to produce the electrical effects we had observed.

The Flow of Lava to the Sea

Everyone involved in the Surtsey expedition came away satisfied. The scientists who had worked from the

airplane were satisfied because their instruments had
worked so well, Vonnegut and Moore because the
lightning was generated without the formation of heavy
rain and hail*, Hughes because the expedition he organized had worked so well, and I because we had found a
positive charge in the Surtsey clouds.

With the background of some of the experiments we
discussed in the last chapter, where the splashing of
sea water on hot lava produced positively charged
clouds, you might jump to the conclusion that the
positively charged clouds at Surtsey were generated by
sea water pouring into the crater and striking molten
lava. Well, I'd like to jump to that conclusion also, but
one really shouldn't.

Are we quite sure that the sea water struck the lava?
I saw it pour into the crater, but how do I know it
wasn't vaporized in the intense heat? And if it did
strike the lava (which I am inclined to believe) why
wasn't the equal and opposite negative charge carried
into the air by the lava when it exploded into ash?
Could it somehow have flowed away to ground? And
how about other mechanisms of charge generation?
Questions like these must be answered before we can
conclude, firmly and definitely, that Surtsey's electricity
was the direct result of sea water striking hot lava.

A conclusive proof of the capacity of sea water to
generate charge upon striking hot lava probably could
be obtained by making potential gradient measurements near the clouds that are produced when molten
lava flows off the land and into the sea. Compared to
the Surtsey eruptions we had seen, this situation would

* Back in Chapter 7 mention was made of Vonnegut's idea
that rain and hail are not necessary for thunderstorm electricity.
Although Surtsey's eruption cloud was not a thunderstorm, it was
interesting to find that rain and hail did not appear to be necessary for volcanic electricity. It would have been just as interesting,
from the point of view of Vonnegut's idea, had negative charge
been found in the Surtsey cloud.

be relatively uncomplicated. There would be no denying that the sea water struck the lava, and the clouds would contain little or no ash.

Surtsey obligingly set up the conditions for this experiment. On the fourth of April 1964 the opening to the sea in Surtsey's crater became blocked with ash. The sea water could not gain entry, the great explosions stopped, and a molten lava lake formed. As in the lava lake in Halemaumau (Chapter 9), beautiful fountains sprayed molten lava over a hundred feet into the air. Later the same day the lake overflowed, and small streams of lava made their way down the sides of the crater and into the sea. Long dense plumes of white cloud rose into the air and were carried off by the wind. These lava flows to the sea continued off and on for several months (Plate XVI).

On the twenty-fourth of July, Sveinbjörn Björnsson of the State Electricity Authority of Iceland, one of the Icelandic scientists who had worked with us on the Surtsey expedition, sailed around Surtsey. He was aboard an Iceland Coast Guard ship which was equipped to measure the potential gradient. As they approached Surtsey they could see the dancing fountains of lava framed against the sky. Molten lava was flowing down around the main peak and into the sea. The cloud plume that rose from the water (Plate XVII) was carried by the wind over the western edge of the island and out to sea. Björnsson had the ship sail around the island and directly toward this cloud plume. The potential gradient had been about normal, but as the ship approached the plume, the gradient began to rise, slowly at first, but then very rapidly, until it reached a maximum of about +3200 volts per meter as they were passing under the plume (Fig. 41).

There was no doubt about it this time. That long horizontal line of cloud carried a positive charge that must have originated back at the source of the cloud,

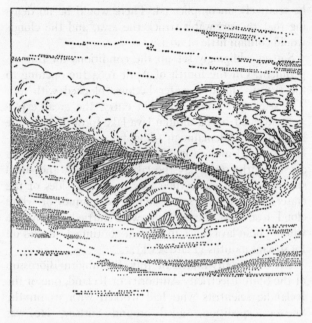

FIG. 41. Under the cloud line stretching westward from the point where Surtsey's lava poured into the sea, ship recorded potential gradient twenty-five times higher than the gradient over open sea.

the splashing of the sea against the molten lava. As the cloud rose from the sea, the concentration of positive charge, according to calculations that were made later, was at least one million elementary charges per cubic centimeter.

Björnsson made two other visits to Surtsey, with a helicopter which landed him directly on the island. He was able to carry his potential gradient meter up to the very edge of glowing streams of liquid lava, and into the dense white clouds that were being generated in great profusion as the lava was quenched by waves along the shore. His findings were the same as before:

the clouds that rose from the sea were highly charged with positive electricity. Negative electricity was never found.

Although Björnsson has shown quite clearly that positively charged clouds can be produced when the sea makes contact with molten lava, the question of the source of the positive charge that we had observed during the violent eruption of Surtsey must remain open. Admittedly, Björnsson's work makes it seem very probable that sea water even there was the cause of the positive charge, but until the questions mentioned earlier are answered, there will remain a gnawing element of doubt.

The Future of Surtsey

In late May of 1965, after a year and a half of activity, Surtsey became quiet. The powerful forces within the earth which had spawned Surtsey looked for another outlet, and in early June the sea began to boil about a third of a mile northeast of Surtsey. The familiar fountains of ash and cloud rocketed skyward and Syrtlingur was born.

On the seventeenth of October Syrtlingur was about 1600 feet in diameter and 160 feet high, but then it, too, became quiet. A week later, under the ceaseless pounding of the ocean waves, its slopes of ash were eaten away and it disappeared into the depths of the sea. Surtsey had been spared that fate because a protective armor of hard lava covered nearly half of its vulnerable interior.

More was yet to come. The day after Christmas the eruptions started again, but this time about a half mile to the southwest of Surtsey. Heavy winter storms prevented Christmas Island from growing very rapidly, but it continued in eruption until August 1966. Then all activity ceased.

A week later a fissure opened on the southeast coast of Surtsey. The island came to life once again as fountains of lava played from four craters to heights of about 450 feet. The volcanic activity had come full circle.

Man has learned much from Surtsey and its eruptions. The new knowledge extends far, far beyond what we had the good fortune to obtain in our study of the electricity in the volcanic clouds. Many other scientists have visited Surtsey; their interests have ranged from chemical changes in the sea to biological studies of life on the new volcanic soil.

A number of research trails have met and are crossing at Surtsey, and those of us involved would be foolish indeed if we did not take cognizance of this fact. At one of these junctions a new and exciting research trail may have been found. The signpost pointing the way does not say volcanic electricity, types of lava, fissure eruptions in the sea, heat flow through volcanic ash, or sea water and electricity. It says, "A key to the past."

The birth of Surtsey and the formation of the volcanic clouds, the struggle with the sea and the coming of life to the new island, are a re-enactment of what must have happened hundreds of times in the distant past. In this event, capsuled in space and time, may be a key that will enable man to open yet another of the doors that obscure our view down that long corridor through which he and the world have evolved.

EPILOGUE

In following the trail from raindrops to volcanoes, we have wandered afar and have seen many strange and wondrous things occurring at the surface of the sea. At this boundary between the air and the sea where meteorology and oceanography meet, our path has led us into and out of several realms of science, including physics, chemistry, and volcanology.

We have crossed the borders from one realm to another silently and unannounced. This is not surprising, for the borders exist only in the mind of man, who has attempted to separate nature into rigid box-like compartments. Nature knows no such compartments. Her realms cannot be separated completely, for part of one is part of the other. They, like the colors in a rainbow, merge smoothly and harmoniously.

I cannot stress this great unity of nature enough. More and more, the scientists of today recognize it, and the merging of nature's realms has been very much in evidence in our travels along the trail in this book. The formation of bubbles in the sea, their rising to and breaking at the surface, the evolution of the film drops and jet drops and their charge, the rising of these drops from the sea and their journey up to the clouds where they have some effect in the formation of rain—this complicated chain of phenomena is but one example. The principles of both physics and chemistry will have to be applied to unravel all the mysteries behind these events.

At the end of a book an author will often attempt to summarize what has been said. This will not be done here. I am not as much concerned with facts about the sea and the air that you may carry away from this book as I am about the attitude toward science and truth that you may develop. I earnestly hope that this book has been a window through which you have had a glimpse of science and scientists. I hope you have sensed just a bit of the excitement, the wonder, and the beauty which accompany the search to understand nature.

Those of us who are engaged in this search have no magic formula to guide us on our way. But we are certain of one thing. It is only by continually asking questions of nature in the way of experiment that we slowly begin to perceive what we call the truth.

SUGGESTED READING

L. J. Battan, *Cloud Physics and Cloud Seeding*. Science Study Series, Doubleday & Company, Inc., 1962, 144 pp.
Written for the non-scientist, this discusses the physics and chemistry of the formation of clouds, rain, snow, and hail.

L. J. Battan, *The Unclean Sky*. Science Study Series, Doubleday & Company, Inc., 1966, 141 pp.
A lucid and timely account of particles in the atmosphere, in particular those which are being introduced by man.

Weatherwise. American Meteorological Society, 45 Beacon Street, Boston, Massachusetts, published bimonthly.
A magazine for students and non-scientists which covers all aspects of the weather.

C. V. Boys, *Soap Bubbles*. Science Study Series, Doubleday & Company, Inc., 1959, 156 pp.
Written in 1902, this has become a classic in science literature. It gives a delightful and clear account of bubbles in the air, and of the formation of drops from fountains.

E. A. Abbott, *Flatland*. Dover Publications, Inc., 1953, 103 pp.
Another classic in science literature, written about 1880. This is a fantasy which describes the inhabitants of a land of two dimensions. With a bit of imagination, the surface of the sea could be thought of as a real-life Flatland.

Oceanus. A quarterly publication of the Woods Hole Oceanographic Institution, Woods Hole, Massachusetts. It can be found in many city and university libraries. The articles, written in a popular style, cover oceanography, marine meteorology, and related subjects.

S. Thorarinsson, *Surtsey*. Almenna Bókafélagid, Reykjavik, Iceland, 1964, 63 pp. plus 46 plates.

An interesting account of the birth of Surtsey, the Icelandic volcanic island. In addition, this book contains 46 magnificent photographs, the majority in full color, of Surtsey in various stages of eruption. Professor Thorarinsson also wrote "Surtsey: Island Born of Fire," *National Geographic*, May 1965.

W. J. Humphreys, *Physics of the Air*. McGraw-Hill Company, Inc., Third Edition 1940, 676 pp.

An advanced text, first published in 1920, and now one of the classics of meteorology. It covers all aspects of atmospheric physics, and discusses in detail optical effects in the atmosphere and the effects on the weather of dust from volcanic eruptions.

B. J. Mason, *The Physics of Clouds*. Oxford at the Clarendon Press, 1957, 481 pp.

An advanced treatise that discusses in detail the physics and chemistry of clouds, rain, snow, and electrical effects in the atmosphere.

N. H. Fletcher, *The Physics of Rainclouds*. Cambridge at the University Press, 1962, 386 pp.

Another advanced treatise which, like Mason's book, contains full discussion of the latest work in the subject. Dozens of references to research articles are given.

INDEX